£7.25

PERGAMON INTERNATIONAL LIBRARY
of Science, Technology, Engineering and Social Studies
The 1000-volume original paperback library in aid of education,
industrial training and the enjoyment of leisure
Publisher: Robert Maxwell, M.C.

CRISIS INTERVENTION:

STUDIES IN COMMUNITY CARE

Publisher's Notice to Educators

THE PERGAMON TEXTBOOK
INSPECTION COPY SERVICE

An inspection copy of any book published in the Pergamon International Library
will gladly be sent without obligation for consideration for course adoption or
recommendation. Copies may be retained for a period of 60 days from receipt and
returned if not suitable. When a particular title is adopted or recommended for
adoption for class use and the recommendation results in a sale of 12 or more
copies, the inspection copy may be retained with our compliments. If after examination the lecturer decides that the book is not suitable for adoption but would like to
retain it for his personal library, then our Educators' Discount of 10% is allowed on
the invoiced price. The Publishers will be pleased to receive suggestions for revised
editions and new titles to be published in this important International Library.

PROBLEMS AND PROGRESS IN DEVELOPMENT
Editor: Jack Kahn

Some other titles in this series

HERBERT, W.L. & JARVIS, F.V.   Marriage Counselling in the Community
HORDERN, A.   Legal Abortion: The English Experience
McCULLOCH, J.W. & PHILIP, A.E.   Suicidal Behaviour
RAVENETTE, A.T.   Dimensions of Reading Difficulties
RENFRE, C.E.   Speech Disorders in Children
VENABLES, E.   Leaving School and Starting Work
KAHN, J.H. with Hester Solomon: Job's Illness: Loss, Grief and Integration

ADDICTIVE BEHAVIORS
An International Journal

Editor-in-Chief, Peter M. Miller, Jackson, Mississippi

ADDICTIVE BEHAVIORS is a professional journal designed to publish original research, theoretical papers and critical reviews in the area of substance abuse. The journal will focus on the problems of alcoholism, drug abuse, smoking and obesity in which psychological and/or physical dependence exists.

INTERNATIONAL JOURNAL OF NURSING STUDIES
Honorary Editor, Dr. K.J.W. Wilson,
University of Birmingham

An international journal concerned with the publication of papers on all aspects of nursing and allied professions throughout the world. The emphasis is on meeting the community's needs for all types of nursing care, on preparing young people for assuming nursing duties and responsibilities and on encouraging all aspects of nursing research.

The terms of our inspection copy service apply to all the above books. Full details of all books listed and specimen copies of journals listed will gladly be sent upon request.

CRISIS INTERVENTION –
STUDIES IN COMMUNITY CARE

J. K. W. MORRICE, M.D., F.R.C.Psych., D.P.M.
(Consultant Psychiatrist, The Ross Clinic, Aberdeen)

PERGAMON PRESS
OXFORD · NEW YORK · TORONTO
SYDNEY · PARIS · FRANKFURT

OXFORD	Pergamon Press Ltd., Headington Hill Hall, Oxford, England
U.S.A.	Pergamon Press Inc., Maxwell House, Fairview Park, Elmsford, New York 10523, U.S.A.
CANADA	Pergamon of Canada Ltd., P.O. Box 9600, Don Mills M3C 2T9, Ontario, Canada
AUSTRALIA	Pergamon Press (Aust.) Pty. Ltd., 19a Boundary Street, Rushcutters Bay, N.S.W. 2011, Australia
FRANCE	Pergamon Press SARL, 24 rue des Ecoles, 75240 Paris, Cedex 05, France
WEST GERMANY	Pergamon Press GmbH, 6242 Kronberg-Taunus, Pferdstrasse 1, Frankfurt-am-Main, West Germany

First edition 1976

Library of Congress Cataloging in Publication Data

Morrice, J K W

Crisis intervention. – Studies in Community Care

(Problems & progress in development series) (Pergamon international library of science, technology, engineering and social studies)

Bibliography: p.

Includes index.

1. Crisis intervention (Psychiatry) – Cases, clinical reports, statistics. I. Title.

RC480.7.C7M67   616.8:9'0250926   75-40029

ISBN 0-08-019742-6

ISBN 0-08-019741-8 pbk.

616.89.

Printed in Great Britain by A. Wheaton & Co. Exeter

CONTENTS

PREFACE AND ACKNOWLEDGEMENTS

'Ideas spring from a source that is not contained within one man's personal life. We do not create them; they create us. To be sure, when we deal in ideas we inevitably make a confession, for they bring to the light of day not only the best that in us lies, but our worst insufficiencies and personal shortcomings as well.'

(C. G. JUNG, *Modern Man in Search of a Soul*)

THE principal aim of this book is to give a straightforward account of Crisis Theory and Crisis Intervention with emphasis upon the part which can be played by non-psychiatrists. The kind of problems which present, the helping agents involved, and the procedures used are discussed mainly in the context of case-histories drawn from life. Personal details and circumstances have been altered in order to disguise identity. The intention is to provide examples and comments of a practical nature. The intricacies of psychopathological speculation are avoided. It is hoped that the book will interest and instruct social workers, nurses, general practitioners, clergymen, school-teachers, probation officers, policemen, members of voluntary organizations such as Marriage Guidance Councils, Telephone Samaritans, and Alcoholics Anonymous – and indeed anyone who finds himself involved with people in trouble.

I am indebted to a number of colleagues of different disciplines who have influenced me directly and indirectly. Some have taken time and trouble to discuss their work and ideas with me. From others I have had the privilege of learning over a period of years. While I am sure each of these colleagues will disagree with some of the statements contained in these pages, they also cannot fail to recognize reflections of their own ideas. I should like to acknowledge the particular debt I owe in this regard to Dr. Maxwell Jones, Professor W. M. Millar, and Dr. J. D. Sutherland. Further, it should be said that, without the stimulation and guidance of Dr. Jack Kahn, the book would not have been written at all. Finally, I take pleasure in recognizing the debt I owe to my wife, Norah, who contrived a wind when I was becalmed in the doldrums of authorship and was a constant help in the actual task of composition.

CHAPTER 1

INTRODUCTION : MENTAL HEALTH AND THE COMMUNITY

AN adolescent is rushed to the casualty department of a general hospital after an overdose of pills; an old woman is found comatose, with no food or heating, in the top floor of a tenement block; a health visitor is faced with a baby who is ill-nourished and badly bruised in the arms of a mother who seems dispirited and distrait. All these situations may be described as emergencies or crises. By the time they happen there has been a failure of caring. There has occurred a breakdown in communication, in responsibility, and in relationships. Early warning signs have gone unheeded by relatives, friends or professional helpers. Perhaps words denoting distress have been ignored or discounted. For one reason or another the family and the community have been unable to foresee or prevent the occurrence of a crisis.

This book considers such events: their nature, how they arise, the people who try to cope with them, and how such crises may be dealt with more effectively. Many of these emergencies may be labelled 'psychiatric' but this is a rather misleading word. Psychiatry is the study and treatment of mental disorders. Psychiatrists are doctors who are generally to be found in psychiatric hospitals and clinics where they treat patients referred to them mainly by other doctors. Some of the people who find themselves in the throes of a social or emotional crisis may well make their way to a psychiatrist. But one of the themes of this book is that some crises can be successfully managed without formal psychiatric intervention. In this sense, therefore, they are not psychiatric. Or they are psychiatric only because they indicate emotional disturbance or involve disruption of social relationships. In such circumstances it may be argued that the mental health of the individual, the family, or the community, has broken down in some way.

As a phrase, 'mental health' is in common use but, as a concept, it is open to different interpretations. The media of communication, particularly television and the cinema, have acquainted the general public with psychiatric disorders and what may be done about them. Plays, documentaries, and other sorts of T.V. programmes impress viewers with the complexity and variability of human nature and suggest the conflicts of love and violence which may exist behind the controlled exteriors of everyday people. At the same time, despite these insights, the public retains a strong tendency to view mental distress as the province of psychiatrists and best avoided by others. Ignorance and fear have built high walls behind which mental illness has been forced to hide for many years. Whatever the root causes, and whether the fault is seen as that of psychiatry or of the community at large, it is true that society was content, until recently, to consign its insane, its misfits, and its deviants to the care (and perhaps the oblivion) of mental institutions. Of course changes have occurred. Indeed they seem to be sweeping us along at an ever-accelerating pace. Public misunderstanding and prejudice about psychiatric disorder and its treatment are still plainly evident, but at least the problems are open for discussion and nowadays interest and concern are replacing the fear and rejection of the past. Mental hospitals too are changing in many hopeful ways and there is a growing commitment, on the part of psychiatric doctors and nurses, to forge working links with the community outside the walls.

However, it must be confessed that the vast majority of mental health services throughout the world are really mental *illness* services. That is to say, they are based on psychiatric hospitals and clinics and most of the work is done within these institutions upon cases already labelled 'psychiatric'. Small notice is taken of opportunities for the prevention of mental illness in outside society, and little time is spent in mental health education or consultation.

It is an agreed fact that suitably constructed and well-staffed units (whether in psychiatric or general hospitals) which possess the resources to treat severe mental illness are a basic essential in any mental health service. It would not be difficult to formulate a convincing argument for a higher level of staffing and for better treatment facilities in such units, many of which carry a heavy burden of patient care. At the same time, there is a growing realization of the tasks and responsibilities which lie outside the ward and the institution. Any modern system of health care must recognize that the patient exists in a social and cultural milieu which influences his falling ill and his prospects of getting better. Mental health workers, who generally gain their therapeutic skills and derive their professional values from the treatment of individual clients, have begun to accept a commitment to the mental health of communities. Few psychiatrists nowadays are content simply to sit in their consulting rooms, dealing with those labelled 'mentally ill', and to ignore the many agencies outside struggling with increasing numbers of disturbed, distressed, and unhappy people. Not that the psychiatrist himself has any ready answers to such problems as crowded divorce courts, abuse of alcohol and drugs, violence in the classroom, or a rising incidence of venereal disease. No one discipline can neglect its own central concern in order to assume the task of reforming society. Clearly psychiatry has no such mandate. In any case, experience has taught the psychiatrist to recognize his limited expertise when he moves outside hospital boundaries. But this should not result in a sense of futility or pessimism about the prospects for community mental health. Rather it should encourage a gathering together of the skills which *are* available and a fostering of co-operation with other professionals and interested members of the public. The promotion of health rather than merely the treatment of disease then becomes a more central concern of all health workers.

The recent re-organization of the National Health Service in Britain reminds us of the constant need for evaluation and planning. To engineer and maintain a suitable administrative structure for such an endeavour demands vision and flexibility. There is presently a pre-occupation with finance, buildings, standardization of equipment, and management efficiency. The size of the whole service, the intricacies of the administrative machine, and the proliferation of committees may bring a feeling of impotence and unimportance to the individual worker in the field. But the re-organization will have failed in its purpose (and the recent expansion of community services will also be of small account) if the importance of the individual patient in his milieu is neglected. The planners hope for an expanded and more integrated mental health service which crosses institutional boundaries. In fact, the range of services already existing in many parts of the country – for example, health centres, day-care facilities, half-way houses, psychological services to schools, children's panels, and departments of forensic psychiatry – gives the opportunity for useful co-operation among different disciplines. In the United States of America the growth in the 1960s of comprehensive community mental health centres, while failing in some regards to meet the high expectations of their protagonists, signalled a vigorous new policy. The very definition of the term 'comprehensive', which spelt out the need for partial hospitalization (e.g. day-care), emergency services around the clock, and consultation and educational services – in addition to customary in-patient and out-patient facilities – awakened mental health professionals to the needs and opportunities around them.

It can be demonstrated that various professionals and laymen, if given the opportunity to meet regularly 'on the job', will come to recognize one another's viewpoints, begin to talk the same language to one another, and find more telling ways of collaborating. The social worker, schoolteacher, vicar, policeman, and family doctor are at present handling the vast majority of the emotionally disturbed. How well it is difficult to tell. It would seem appropriate, however, that the resources which are available should be marshalled in such a way as to render their endeavours more effective. Legislative and administrative blue-prints have their limits. The mere multiplication of staff numbers can also prove unrewarding. Ideals too can be made to look foolish by interdisciplinary rivalry and misunderstanding. Much might be achieved by broader and better training facilities with opportunities for mutual education across disciplinary boundaries. In particular, there seems to be a great need for education of the helping professionals in what may be termed 'psycho-dynamic awareness', that is, the ability to recognize, understand, and make an appropriate response to emotional distress.

It seems that many people who are suffering from emotional disturbance and who are referred to psychiatrists are in the throes of some kind of social crisis. The resources of the immediate family and friends have been strained or exceeded and those concerned turn to the medical services. Consequently there is an understandable tendency in our society for a 'patient' to be identified and a 'diagnosis' made. The problem presented is placed in a medical or psychiatric context and labelled 'anxiety state' or 'alcoholism' or 'schizophrenia'. The person is considered ill and can then be accepted as suitable for the treatment of his symptoms or disturbed behaviour. He may then receive advice or, more often, a prescription for pills. If he is referred to the psychiatric services he may be given psychotherapy or may find himself an inpatient in hospital. It is not unusual for the precipitating crisis to be noted merely to be discounted and the disturbance in the home or at work to be ignored. The conflict, in such an event, is considered to exist within the patient himself and that becomes the focus of concern. The other conflict which may be present in the family is thought to be secondary, irrelevant, or beyond reach. However, a body of opinion exists which regards the mentally disturbed, or at least some categories of them, as suffering from disturbances which are essentially interpersonal in nature. That is to say, the disturbance is viewed as occurring not so much 'inside' the individual as 'outside' — in his interpersonal relationships with the people around him and who are important to him. Supporters of this view point to the connection between stressful life events and subsequent episodes of mental disorder. They assert that social crisis is a frequent precipitant of emotional upset and of mental illness, and that therapeutic intervention aimed at the resolution of the crisis is valuable and effective.

Clearly it would be foolish to set one view against the other. They are complementary. At a basic level, factors which are environmental and those which are constitutional are inextricably interwoven. At a practical level, there may be little choice in the matter. For example, an aggressive outburst on the part of an acutely disturbed schizophrenic in his own home, no matter how caused, demands immediate intervention. The patient may be so excited and deluded and the other members of the family so distressed, that the injection of a tranquillizing agent into the patient is the only available method of control. He may then require to be committed to hospital. But even in such a case, although an understanding of the interactions in the family leading to the emergency is not immediately available, it should be sought at an early opportunity. Such understanding may be crucial in any longer-term plans that involve the patient and his family. Moreover, the more the patient's intrapsychic disturbance can also be uncovered and understood, the better is the therapist's comprehension of the total situation and what changes may usefully be attempted. But understanding of the patient's deeper thoughts and feelings may be difficult to achieve. The argument therefore is not the denial of the ultimate importance of individual psychopathology. Rather the opinion is being offered that, within the limits of our working conditions, e.g. the shortage of time and skills, it may be expedient in *treating* the emotionally disturbed to be more concerned with social than with intra-psychic factors. This is particularly so in emergency referrals, where an approach which seeks to uncover interpersonal disturbances and support the family's own resources in resolving them, can be demonstrably effective and clearly appropriate.

Some of the recent interest in emergency and community psychiatry arises from the desire to keep patients out of hospital. There is much to be said for this on the grounds that admission as a psychiatric in-patient is costly, regressive, and diminishes the person's self-esteem. When in-patient treatment is completed, the individual has to find entry again to his family circle and his community. The stigma of mental illness remains evident in society and can cause embarrassment and difficulty. At the same time, the disadvantages of hospitalization should not be emphasized to the exclusion of its benefits. Appropriate treatment of the patient demands an intelligent appraisal of his resources and needs, as well as those of his family. The availability of skilled help, including professional care, will also be a major factor. A psychiatric unit which has skilled nurses and social workers available to support patients in their own homes has less need to find in-patient beds for them. While it would be naïve to reformulate mental illness as simply a social disorder and its treatment as social intervention, nevertheless the large old mental hospital stands as a monument to the folly of cutting off patients from their families and their communities.

Effective treatment of the mentally disturbed in the community means the marshalling of resources in a different fashion from that traditionally practised. The psychiatrist finds himself within a new framework and needs to play a somewhat different role. The psychiatric nurse, social worker, clinical psychologist and others who have been hospital-bound in the past need to gain confidence in the setting of outside society, collaborating with general practitioner, health visitor, clergyman, and non-professional worker. Conversely, institutions and agencies in the community must accept more responsibility and find more active support for the disturbed and the deviant in their midst. It should be made quite clear that society's mental health needs cannot be matched with *professional* resources. The present dilemma of local authority social work departments in Britain demonstrates this fact: accepting a sea of problems tends to swamp the boat. It should be frankly admitted therefore that to provide suitable alternatives to hospitalization demands a high level of competent staff which few centres at the present time can provide. The answer seems to lie in the fuller use of two groups of people: firstly non-professionals, who will need guidance, training, and on-going support; and secondly, professionals (such as hospital nurses, health visitors, and general practitioners) who are generally either ill-trained or poorly utilized in mental health work. The corollary of this is that skilled mental health workers, such as psychiatrist and experienced social workers, will be required to spend more time in indirect services such as consultation and education. One immediately rewarding area for such joint activity is crisis intervention.

All this presupposes an interest, concern, or commitment on the part of some members of society who, in past times, it may be fairly said, often failed to show such attitudes. One thinks of school-teachers, policemen, clergymen, and lawyers. The daily work of such important individuals brings them into contact with social needs and emotional disturbances; but, preoccupied as they are with matters of discipline, law enforcement, moral exhortation, and the demands of business, their particular opportunities for crisis intervention are generally neglected. Yet often it is just such non-medical professionals, operating as it were in the front-line of society, who should be able to deal quickly with at least some cases of emotional distress, deviant behaviour, or family disruption. 'He gives twice who gives quickly' is never more true than in the case of psychiatric emergency. A helping hand, even if relatively unskilled, applied in a timely and understanding way, may reverse the mounting catastrophe or the descent into mental breakdown. The chapters which follow discuss the nature of such emergencies and how intervention may be offered constructively.

CHAPTER 2

WHAT IS AN EMERGENCY?

TO find an acceptable short definition of a psychiatric emergency is difficult. A questionnaire circulated to 154 psychiatric emergency services in the United States of America several years ago demonstrated this quite clearly.[1] Only twenty of these psychiatric units had arrived at formal definitions and, of these, not one was really comprehensive. Most of the psychiatric services surveyed indicated that they were guided by commonsense considerations and tended to view as an emergency the presentation of anyone who seemed dangerous to himself or to others. They also accepted for treatment any person whose psychiatric condition appeared urgent in the sense that there was obvious need for control or protection.

Information derived from this questionnaire, subsequently corroborated by experience of crisis intervention in Britain and the U.S.A., demonstrates that the kinds of behaviour consistently accepted as constituting a psychiatric emergency are relatively few in number. They may be listed as follows:

1. Attempted suicide (also called para-suicide).
2. Assault.
3. Destruction of property.
4. Extreme anxiety amounting to panic.
5. Bizarre behaviour evoking fear.

The general public recognizes such behaviour as constituting an emergency or crisis. If the affected individual does not seek help for himself, then a friend, relative, or helping agent tends to seek it on his behalf. Such considerations imply that a *psychiatric* emergency is usually also a *social* emergency. But clearly all social emergencies are not psychiatric in nature. It also appears that behaviour which attracts the label 'emergency' is that which carries a threat to the community — e.g. assault, or property damage, or, perhaps less obviously, a suicide attempt.

The suggestion has been made that a large proportion of referrals to a psychiatric service are in some sort of social crisis.[2] Certainly, in the case of emergency referrals, social difficulties or disturbing life-events are usually quite evident. But, even in the case of long-standing psychiatric illness, a referral may be occasioned by problems that are more social than simply medical in nature. It may be apparent on enquiry that the crisis has occurred because the family's limit of tolerance has been exceeded. Even so, the precipitant may not be the patient's behaviour, which remains much as always, but rather some untoward event which has upset the balance of forces in the household. This may be a bereavement, illness of another family member, or a loss of income, In such circumstances, to admit the patient to residential care may be expedient and sometimes appropriate. But the family also needs help; and given adequate support may be able to retain the patient at home. In this way the family may achieve a better level of organization within itself, and thus enjoy a sense of successful coping rather than having to carry a burden of failure.

Of course the doctor, social worker, nurse, or whoever happens to be in the position of intervening must remain sensitive to a family's degree of stress. An example may be cited of a young disturbed schizophrenic whose odd behaviour, including open masturbation, was tolerated by his family for many months. However, when he started to make sexual advances to both his sister and his mother, their alarm prevented them from continuing their support and supervision. Return of the young man to hospital was then inevitable.

Events which precipitate emergencies

What are the kinds of crucial events which trigger off emergencies? This question does not imply that all emergencies are related to identifiable events, nor that environmental stress is more important in such states than intrapsychic processes. But it does seem possible to identify a number of familiar difficulties which precipitate people into personal crises and often lead to their referral to a helping agency.

Figures derived from the Day Hospital of the Ross Clinic, Aberdeen, show that a majority of patients treated there are recognizably in some kind of social crisis.[3] Of 266 consecutive admissions, a significant life crisis leading to referral was identified in all but seven. These crises were categorized and are shown in Table I.

Similar data derived from a number of emergency psychiatric services in the U.S.A.[1] show that the problems which commonly precipitate emergencies

TABLE I

All crises identified in 266 admissions to Day Hospital

Nature of crisis	No.	Per cent
Interpersonal difficulty in the family	249	51
Antisocial behaviour	30	6
Work problem	110	22
Financial problem	35	7
Physical illness	22	4
Bereavement	27	6
Accident	4	1
Pregnancy	8	2
Other	5	1
Total crises:	490	100

TABLE II

Nature of problems cited by 85 Emergency Services, U.S.A.

Nature of problem	No. of times cited
Family conflict, including marital discord and impending divorce	51
Excessive use of alcohol	27
Problems relating to job or income	19
Bereavement or grief reaction	16
Exacerbation of chronic mental illness	12
Problems of adolescence	6
Problems of old age	5
School problems	4
Medical illness	4
Separation from familiar environment	3
Homosexual panic	3
Legal charges	2
Postpartum depression	2
Postoperative reaction	2

tend to group themselves into familiar categories. Table II shows the factors mentioned more than once by eighty-five such services.

Despite the differences in patient populations, in cultural background, and in terminology, there are obvious similarities in the types of problem noted and in their incidence. Disagreements and quarrels within the family figure largely and comprise the most frequent precipitating event. Problems at work or of a financial nature loom large. Bereavement and excessive use of alcohol are also prominent factors.

Attempted suicide as a presenting emergency

One crisis which is increasing in frequency is that of deliberate self-injury or attempted suicide. Its rising incidence, now of epidemic proportions, is of great concern to casualty departments, general medical units, and psychiatric clinics. Reliable statistics of suicidal behaviour are difficult to obtain and most figures are likely to be underestimates. It is suggested that in Britain each year 5500 people commit suicide — that is equivalent to one person in 10,000 of population. In the U.S.A. the number of recorded suicides is over 20,000 per annum or one in each hundred deaths. It is accepted that the number of attempted suicides is at least ten times, and more likely twenty times, the figure for completed suicides. In Britain the incidence of attempted suicide has been calculated at a conservative estimate to be 1 per 1000 population per annum. It is reckoned to account for some 15 per cent of acute medical admissions and entails at least 50,000 psychiatric consultations per annum.

Kessel[4] has pointed out that the term 'attempted suicide' is inappropriate and should be discarded. He emphasizes that the majority of such acts are acknowledged by the individuals themselves to carry no real intention of serious harm. Many studies since have demonstrated how often the act of self-injury or self-poisoning has the purpose of drawing attention to personal problems, trivial or serious, not of ending life. By no means all attempted suicides are to be considered failed suicides. The term 'parasuicide' has been suggested, therefore, as being a less dramatic and more truthful description of behaviour which may be a call for help or a gesture of defiance. Few individuals caught up in this crisis seem to have a clearly formulated idea of killing themselves. On occasion, however, the gesture backfires and death occurs accidentally.

It is worth remembering that the real risk to life may bear no relationship to the apparent 'seriousness' of the attempt. A trivial overdose may be swallowed with more serious intent than a poisonous dose taken in the presence of concerned members of the family. It is therefore important to make an assessment of the individual's intent and not simply consider what he took or did. For example, people who are severely depressed are a high-risk group. Such a person may have a determined wish to die and yet, because of the retardation of thought and action consequent upon his illness, make a poor attempt at self-destruction. In such circumstances one might mistakenly construe the behaviour as a gesture rather than a serious attempt. Suicidal behaviour does not fit readily into neat categories. Each individual needs individual consideration. Some people are suicidal for only a limited time; others are prone to repeat attempts and this seems particularly true of those with personality disorders and those addicted to drugs and alcohol. Often there seems to be an element of risk-taking in the behaviour, as if the person was, in a sense, gambling with death and leaving to fate the responsibility of whether to live or die.

Fallacies

It is still commonly but mistakenly believed that people who talk about suicide never kill themselves. In fact there is grave danger in ignoring hints and threats. There is reason to believe that 80 per cent of suicides give clear warning of their intent. As many as half of them, it has been shown, consulted their doctors shortly beforehand. Indeed the suggestion has been made that failure of relative or doctor to recognize and respond to the individual's plea is itself a factor in the precipitation of the suicide. Another current fallacy is that suicidal behaviour is associated with social class. In fact it seems to be quite 'democratic' in its distribution and is represented proportionately among all social levels. It seems true, however, that certain professional groups are particularly prone; for example, the medical profession carries a heavy incidence of suicide. A further false belief is that everyone who is suicidal is mentally ill. In fact many people who attempt suicide are unhappy rather than ill. Distress should not be equated with psychiatric disorder although, of course, the latter may supervene if the situation becomes overwhelming.

Studies of suicidal behaviour

A recent investigation of deliberate self-injury in Sussex, England,[5] indicated that poisoning with barbiturates was the commonest method used and the highest incidence was in young married women. In 36 per cent of cases, mental disturbances and unhappy love affairs were causative factors. Ten per cent of the patients studied were thought to be suffering from personality disorders.

A number of careful studies of suicidal behaviour have been conducted in Edinburgh, Scotland, in recent years. One carried out by Kennedy and Kreitman[6] is of particular interest since it considered parasuicide in general practice and not (as in most other studies) in people admitted to hospital. This investigation showed that 1 in 400 adult citizens of Edinburgh experienced such an episode in 1970. Moreover, among younger women and in certain socially disturbed areas of the city, the incidence was as high as 1 in 200. There are no grounds for supposing that Edinburgh is very different from other large cities. Parasuicide is therefore a problem of major importance.

Another study conducted in the General Hospital, Birmingham, England was of self-poisoning in a group of adolescents. White,[7] who made the investigation, found that 70 per cent of the patients were complaining of interpersonal difficulties, although not all of these appeared serious. For example, a 16-year old girl, following a row with her boy-friend over the way her hair had been cut, swallowed 50 aspirin tablets. Other cases, however, demonstrated situations of severe domestic stress, difficulties at school, or the presence of very low self-esteem. Of this adolescent group, 40 per cent showed no demonstrable psychiatric disorder. It was thought that 32 per cent had depressive reactions, but no one was diagnosed as suffering from a psychotic depression.

Categories

Shneidman and Farberow[8,9] who are authorities in this field, suggest four main categories of suicidal crisis. These may be described as follows:

1. Impulsive suicidal behaviour. This occurs in the heat of anger or other strong emotion. The disturbance is of a temporary nature but the possibility of tragic outcome cannot be ignored.
2. Life is no longer worth living. The individual feels he is no longer wanted or needed; his existence has become meaningless; life is difficult, gloomy, and pointless. Suicide seems a logical step.
3. Serious or painful illness. A person who is in constant pain or who be-

lieves he has an incurable disease may seek death as an escape from suffering or to avoid burdening others.

4. 'Communication attempt'. The underlying motive is not to die but to give a message, offer a plea, or seek to alter the behaviour of others.

These four types, like the two main categories of suicide and attempted suicide themselves are distinct and yet they overlap. It is likely that most people who commit suicide do intend to die. At the other extreme, many so-called attempted suicides are histrionic demonstrations which often appear pointless and tend to arouse irritation and resentment in the busy medical and nursing staff who have to deal with them. But in the middle range the distinction gets blurred and the nature of the act and of the intent may be difficult to determine with any certainty. Generally it is difficult to view suicidal behaviour of any kind other than as a sign of unhappiness or despair. Examination of individual cases may highlight the act as the climax of a series of personal crises which might have been interrupted and resolved if suitable intervention had been available.

Prevention

For suicide to be prevented, the risk must be recognized. The individual who is prone to self-destruction may be identifiable if the people around are willing to ask questions and listen to the answers. It is quite likely that such a person will give notice of his intentions directly or indirectly. Many telling indications relate to those illnesses which carry a high risk of suicide. For example, feelings of guilt, hopelessness, or unworthiness, which often accompany depressive illness, should always arouse concern. Where such symptoms occur in a setting of alcohol or drug dependence, or where marked personality disorder exists, the risk of suicidal behaviour is high. Thus early recognition and prompt treatment of psychiatric disorders like acute depression, schizophrenia, and alcoholism are of great importance in prevention; the non-professional helper should not hesitate to seek skilled advice if features of such disorders are evident.

Knowledge of other criteria may be helpful when the risk is being assessed. For example, two high-risk age-groups emerge from the collected statistics. The first is composed of elderly people, who have been bereaved, live alone, or have little in the way of social support. The second group consists of young people who show evidence of personality disorder and dependence on alcohol or drugs. In both groups the risk is higher if there is a previous history of suicidal behaviour. The recent loss of a loved one by death or divorce, or the anniversary of such a loss, also raises the risk. On the other hand the likelihood is reduced by the presence of relatives and friends who are concerned and supportive. In their absence, a helper who is willing to listen sympathetically may avert self-destructive behaviour.

As long ago as 1897 Durkheim pointed out that suicide, although a highly personal and individual act, was explicable only by taking account of the state of the society in which the person lived. Serious faults in the social structure led to an increase in suicide; on the other hand, the better integrated an individual was with family and society the less likely he would be to take his life. These observations seem even more relevant today in the unstable state of our society. It is generally accepted in principle that the prevention of social isolation and the integration of individuals at risk are worthwhile aims; but how does one achieve them? How does one first identify and then establish links between people who are lonely and distressed and those who are willing and able to help? People who are lonely and in trouble but who are also unknown to family doctor or clergyman are unlikely to get the support they need. It was recognition of this situation that prompted the Telephone Samaritans to set up their organization. The subsequent response of the public indicates the size and intensity of the need. The help offered by the Samaritans consists of 'befriending'. By sharing the person's despair, they lighten his burden. When more skilled help is required, the client may be referred to doctor, lawyer, or social worker. But it seems that often it is the simple availability of another human being which is life-saving.

The Suicide Prevention Center in Los Angeles was set up to deal with the problem of suicide and collect information about it. One suggestion made by the workers there is that, in most cases, suicidal ideas are of brief duration. A service immediately available at the time of crisis will result in many being dissuaded from the act.

Of course it would be foolish to suggest that crisis intervention is the whole answer to suicidal behaviour. Whether the individual is mentally ill or simply very unhappy, there are likely to be difficulties in interpersonal relationships which cannot be resolved quickly and easily. Moreover, some people showing suicidal behaviour are so disturbed in their personalities and backgrounds that they present a formidable challenge to the professional agents who may try to treat and rehabilitate them. Others may reveal by their suicidal behaviour a family situation which responds readily enough to therapeutic intervention, but may require lengthy follow-up and support, for example, by social worker or health visitor, to maintain the improvement. Nevertheless, the crisis of self-injury may give the opportunity for a change of attitude and behaviour that enhances the relationship between the individual and his family and may signify a new beginning.

Aggressive acts presenting as emergencies

The person who is dangerous to himself is much more common in emergency referrals than the person dangerous to others. Yet the notion is well established that the mentally ill are to be feared because of their assaultive tendencies. It is true that an acute schizophrenic, for example, may respond to hallucinatory voices by offering violence to someone at hand. But the incidence of such behaviour, even in psychiatric hospitals, is very small. Moreover, the more liberally run the hospital, the less aggressive behaviour there is to control. Unfortunately newspapers and television are quick to report acts of violence and sometimes headlines are slanted in a way which is detrimental to the mentally ill. The fantasies of the general public are fed with visions of sexual maniacs and homicidal lunatics that are quite unrealistic. It is a sobering thought to remember that, if you are to be murdered, the person most likely to do so is a member of your own family! One of the unfortunate consequences of the distorted picture of the mentally disturbed given by the communication media is society's consequent fear which provides an obstacle to the easy acceptance of community programmes and placements of recovered patients in outside society.

Aggressive behaviour often seems to result from the individual's own feelings of fear or alarm. If the helper, whether it be policeman, nurse, or neighbour, can gain the disturbed person's confidence, resistive or assaultive behaviour is unlikely. However, the possibility of aggressive behaviour as part of a crisis, or being directed towards the person intervening in a crisis, should be kept in mind.

When assaultive or destructive behaviour occurs, the police are generally involved. Despite the fact that the policeman is seldom well-trained in dealing with the mentally disturbed he often functions well when confronted with someone he can clearly identify as ill. It is still evident that mental health personnel and police officers do not always understand one another. On the one hand, attempts at educating the police have tended to focus on serious mental

illness and have largely ignored the characteristics of minor emotional and behavioural disturbances. On the other hand, the police, by long experience,
have learned techniques of handling disturbed people that might usefully be
heeded by mental health professionals. It is plain that anyone seeking to intervene in a crisis involving an aggressive or frightened individual, should be
aware of the necessity of giving the person a clear message, neither threatening nor ambiguous, but rather attempting to enlighten and reassure.

Extreme anxiety presenting as an emergency

Normal anxiety is something everyone knows about. Facing an important
interview, an examination, a public performance, or a surgical operation will
produce in most people a feeling of tremulousness, a sense of unpleasant anti-
cipation, and various physical symptoms such as rapid heart-beats, frequency
of micturition, and abdominal discomfort. The cause is understood and the
anxiety subsides when the occasion is past. Neurotic anxiety, on the other
hand, arises from sources which are often not apparent to the individual; in
any event, the feeling is disproportionate in intensity and duration and inter-
feres with daily living. A chronic state of anxiety may lead to dependence on
alcohol or drugs and may underlie other psychiatric disorders. Abnormal anxiety experienced acutely and amounting to a state of panic may occur and
present as an emergency. Quite often the basis of such a state is a phobia,
which is a condition of acute anxiety evoked by specific situations or objects,
for example, fear of open or closed spaces, of heights, of travelling, or of cats.
Anxiety may become so compelling that the sufferer restricts his life in order
to avoid the frightening situation. Hence the so-called 'housebound house-
wife' who is unable to leave her home except perhaps when accompanied by
husband or parent.

Severe anxiety, no matter how irrational it may be, is a most distressing experience. The sufferer may feel he is about to die or go insane, may feel de-
personalized, faint, or go rushing from the room in panic. A young male nurse
awoke one night in a state of acute anxiety, sweating, breathless and with his
heart thumping loudly. He concluded he was having a heart attack, jumped
from bed in a panic, and *ran* at speed to a hospital a half-mile distant. Later
he was able to laugh at his absurd behaviour. At the time he was in a state of
distress and in no way open to explanation.

The presence of someone the individual can trust, who is not impatient with or disparaging of the sufferer's terror, may help to control the situation. The administration of a sedative or tranquillizer is helpful. But probably the only real answer to the problem is to refer the individual to where the condition can be investigated and suitably treated by psychotherapy, drugs, or behaviour therapy.

Bizarre behaviour presenting as an emergency

Nowadays bizarre behaviour may be due to a variety of causes — mental illness, drugs, or a current craze of the young. The kind of odd behaviour that produces fear and alarm and presents as an emergency is most likely to arise from psychiatric disorder of a serious nature. Very acute episodes of psychosis are rare but may contain a real element of danger for the person afflicted and those around him. Urgent and positive action is necessary and is best carried out by trained personnel.

One day a young man suddenly announced to those around him in the office where he worked that he was the new Messiah. He jumped through the window and ran down the crowded streets discarding his clothes as he went, predicting the end of the world, and calling upon the startled on-lookers to repent of their sins. He was suffering from an acute attack of schizophrenia and, admitted urgently to hospital, responded very well to treatment.

Sometimes, because of confusion, delirium, or delusions, the individual is wildly unco-operative and some measure of restraint and compulsion is necessary. As has already been suggested, most people who are mentally disturbed use violence only when they themselves become frightened. Clear and simple explanation of what one is about is always worthwhile and deception should be avoided at all costs. Competent professional help should be sought immediately. This may bring into play the policeman, general practitioner, mental welfare officer, casualty medical officer, or psychiatrist. In Britain the provisions of the Mental Health Act are generally sufficient to enable those concerned to bring the mentally ill person into immediate care. Urgent admission to hospital may be effected under Section 29 of the Act (in Scotland, Section 30) which requires the recommendation of a single medical practitioner and the application of a relative or the mental welfare officer. Also useful is Section 136 (in Scotland, Section 104) which allows a constable to remove to a place of safety (i.e. hospital) a person whom he finds in a public place and who appears to be mentally disordered and in immediate need of care and control. Compulsory powers are also conferred by the National Assistance Act whereby a medical officer may certify that removal of a person to hospital is necessary on the grounds of prevention of injury to health or serious nuisance to others.

While no one would wish to use compulsory powers to compel an individual into hospital against his wishes, and generally every attempt is made to avoid such a step, nevertheless such action may be life-saving. It should also be remembered that a crisis of this nature which disturbs the family situation may also present an opportunity for constructive intervention.

CHAPTER 3

CRISIS THEORY

THIS term is applied to a body of knowledge which has grown up around the subject of acute stress in individuals and groups. Crisis theory is concerned with how such disturbances arise, their course, their effect on behaviour, and how therapy or guidance can help or hinder. The principles of crisis intervention are derived very largely from the work of Gerald Caplan and his colleagues at Harvard.[10,11] The concepts involved, while still largely unfamiliar to most medical practitioners, must strike a chord of recognition in the minds of many social workers who (even if unaware of the fact) have been putting such principles into practice for years.

Definition of a crisis

In Caplan's view, a crisis is a transitional period or a turning point in life. It presents the individual concerned with the opportunity for acquiring greater mastery and for achieving personality growth, on the one hand, or, on the other, the risk of increased vulnerability and mental breakdown. A crisis is the experience of being confronted with an unfamiliar obstacle in life's path. The familiar resources and past experience of the individual come under test and may be found wanting. He may need help in surmounting the obstacle and in continuing his journey successfully. A crisis can therefore present a challenge to customary habits and, if successfully met, become a stimulus to fruitful innovation and further development. But if the person's customary methods of problem-solving fail and he receives inadequate or inappropriate help in meeting the impasse, he becomes disorganized and may develop an acute anxiety state, depression, or other disabling disorder.

Two categories

There are recognizable two main categories of crisis. One is called 'developmental' and refers to the belief that an individual's personality develops through a number of phases or so-called transitional periods which cause emotional upset at the time. This kind of crisis is one which most people are familiar with or must face on their way through life. Developmental crises include the first day at school, leaving home, getting married, the menopause, and retiral from work.

The second category is 'accidental' and refers to hazards in life which are less expected. This includes physical illness or injury, loss of employment, failure in business, or divorce.

Outcome

The outcome of a crisis is influenced by many factors. Some are within the individual himself in the sense of being dependent on his innate abilities, his past experience, and his qualities of personality. Others are derived more from the society and culture in which he lives, for example how stable it is and what values it propounds. Still other factors seem to be matters of chance. One may picture the person in crisis as being exposed to a complex field of forces, inside and outside himself, which pull one way and then another, and may draw him into a state of helplessness. Characteristic of such a state is the evocation of memories of previous stresses and the feelings which accompanied them. As a consequence there is a risk – sometimes it seems almost a compulsion – to repeat the former behaviour, no matter how unwise or unsuccessful it proved to be previously.

The phases of a crisis

Professor Caplan describes a crisis as occurring in three successive phases.

1. Impact

The individual's customary coping mechanisms fail and signs of stress and strain appear. He may experience feelings of bewilderment and confusion. He may try to wish the event away, pretending it did not really happen after all. He may then engage in attempts to lead his normal life which prove ineffectual.

2. Recoil

This second phase is characterized by increasing evidence of disorganization. The subject is in the grip of uncomfortable emotions — anger, guilt, shame — and his attention is withdrawn from the concerns of everyday existence. Meaningless activity and incompetent functioning serve to increase tension and lead to feelings of impotence. Physical signs and symptoms appear. — agitation, fatigue, insomnia.

3. Adjustment and Adaptation

If resources within and around the individual can be mobilized, the problem is reduced or even removed. A breakthrough instead of a breakdown may be achieved by simply finding a new view or a different definition of the problem. A fresh angle can bring a novel solution. Certain circumstances may be altered or environmental stresses modified. The presenting problem may be broken up and found to be manageable after all when dealt with piecemeal. Or it may be necessary to adopt an active process of resignation and a conscious reduction of demands. Things which cannot be changed are accepted as inevitable. Other parts of the problem may then, with further thought and action, become soluble. Alternative ways of satisfying needs may appear.

Resolution

In most cases a crisis is resolved within 4 to 6 weeks. It is true that the solution may not be complete within this period, but the state of high tension and disorganization has come to an end. This means that the individual has accomplished certain psychological tasks, has mastered negative feelings, and has demonstrated ability to cope by taking action. When the problem is settled by means of a foolish compromise or neurotic manoeuvre, however, a further crisis lies in wait around the corner. When no satisfactory resolution takes place, instead of an emotionally strengthening experience, the crisis leads to a lower level of social competence and the individual risks precipitation into the state of major disorganization we call mental illness.

It is necessary to emphasize that the stages of crisis just described are part of a theory and not proven fact. Implications may be drawn which require further testing before they can be fully accepted. Nevertheless, as Lewin has said, there is nothing more practical than a good theory. It is the view of many workers that Crisis Theory offers a useful framework within which brief methods of therapy or guidance may be offered to those in distress by relatively unsophisticated personnel.

Crisis intervention

The optimistic message conveyed by practitioners of crisis intervention is that we are not necessarily the prisoners of our immutable personalities. We can learn to make wiser, healthier, and more responsible choices at critical periods of our lives. But often we need support and help to do so successfully.

So far, crisis has been described in terms of the individual. But this is an artificial view of things. Crises involve families, work groups, and neighbourhoods. A person does not meet his crisis alone. He is helped or hindered by his wife, his workmates, and his friends. It is a matter of everyday experience that minor emergencies are successfully handled within the family circle. But sometimes the resources of family or friends are not enough and outside aid is sought. This may be requested from family doctor, clergyman, lawyer, marriage guidance counsellor, or social worker. How motivated and prepared are all these people for intervention in a social emergency? How far are they aware of the opportunity offered by a crisis situation for constructive change and to what extent do they recognize that successful resolution depends upon available and timely help?

A caring society

Insofar as our society is a caring society there appears to be a range of people or a spectrum of helpers to whom an individual may turn in an emergency. Immediate family and friends are generally the first to be involved, but this is not so in every case. Certain types of behaviour or certain situations may call other agents quickly into play — for example, the policeman, schoolteacher, or casualty medical officer. There are a number of informal care-givers in any community, who are more obvious perhaps in rural and village society than in large cities. One thinks of the postman who delivers messages and even medicines as well as mail; the motherly district nurse who listens to confidences from many families in her neighbourhood; even perhaps the friendly barmaid who dispenses warm sympathy with the beer. There are also agencies like the

Salvation Army, Samaritans, Alcoholics Anonymous, Synanon, Marriage Guidance, and many other organizations directed at specific groups of people in need. Finally come the care-giving professionals, recognized as such, but with whom contact is generally formal and systematized, for example, the priest, social worker, probation officer, or psychiatrist.

It is clear then that the society in which we live possesses resources and agencies, formal and informal, professional and non-professional, to which a person in the throes of a crisis can turn. Despite evidence to the contrary (for example, the reluctance of the general public to help at a street accident, or intervene in a 'mugging') there exists a great deal of goodwill and good neighbourliness in modern communities. However, it may not always be easily tapped by the person in need, who may be in a state of alarm or bewilderment and unable to act rationally even in seeking assistance. It is therefore worth remembering that the timing of intervention is just as important as the quality. While it is true that a psychiatrist can generally be expected to be in possession of more knowledge and skill than the average citizen, the latter may still be of greater use and value to the person in crisis. After all, it may take days or even weeks for a psychiatrist to become available to the individual concerned; but a relatively unskilled helper who is immediately available can intervene effectively because the time is right.

Practical considerations

There are practical points worth emphasizing in the handling of personal emergencies.

1. Intervention is more likely to be successful if it occurs during the acute phase of the crisis rather than when the crisis is past, by which time the individual or the family have reached some form of compromise and are less open to change. The agency involved should therefore ensure that it can be contacted easily and that there are helpers prepared to act quickly.
2. The helper should try to 'stay with the crisis'. It may be necessary to see the client daily rather than weekly. But it should be kept in mind that the commitment to the client is over a relatively short period of time. Longer-term therapy may or may not be necessary, but it is not part of crisis intervention, as such. The latter is generally to be thought

of as five or six visits over 10 days rather than regularly spaced appointments taking place over 12 months.

3. As far as possible the agent marshals support from family, neighbours, and friends. The object is to keep the individual in his home and in his family setting. It may be necessary to seek help from other agencies in order to make this possible, for example, the home-help service, meals-on-wheels, or health visitor.

4. A person in the throes of a crisis is more than usually susceptible and dependent. This gives an opportunity for dealing with the actual problems which later may be distorted or concealed. Some helpers or therapists — even professional ones — fear the consequences of encouraging over-dependency. Such a relationship, it is felt, is burdensome to the helper and also may disable the client from standing on his own feet. Such anxiety is generally groundless as the dependency is of a temporary nature only.

5. The object of the exchanges between helper and client is the encouragement of honest talk, open expression of feeling, and the maintenance of hope. The actual events and issues of the emergency should be faced as straightforwardly as possible, including the fact that no certain assurance of outcome is guaranteed.

6. The role of intervener is active rather than passive or neutral. In what may be called 'brief therapy' a more directive approach is often necessary to oppose regressive or self-destructive behaviour. A reality-based but reassuring style is generally to be aimed at and rigid adherence to preconceived notions of therapy is better avoided. It has been said, 'Whatever works is useful'.

7. The integrity of the family may demand practical support. Adequate rest for key members should be ensured. There may be good reason for modification or exchange of customary roles, for example, a daughter may assume household duties instead of her mother, or husband take over the cooking from his wife. Besides this, the intervener should be sensitive to scapegoating in the family or the tendency to engage in an endless attribution of blame.

8. Such help as is available should be made use of and efforts at 'pseudo-independence' countered. It should be made plain that to seek necessary help is a sign of strength, not of weakness.

9. The helping-agent should not spend too much time in analysing why the family has failed, but rather encourage meaningful planning and action

as a way towards a solution to present difficulties. The current situation, not past mistakes or memories (although these have relevance), is the area on which attention is focused. It seems valuable to emphasize the 'educational' rather than the 'psychological' approach in discussing the crisis, its boundaries, and the tasks involved in coping with it. Any tendency on the part of the client to withdraw or deny (for example, by abandoning his job or going on holiday) should be resisted.

10. The termination of the agent's relationship with the client is foreseen from the very beginning, but there is no need for a stamp of finality. In a future emergency the individual should feel able to call for help again. In some cases, because of overwhelming stress or the particular vulnerability of the individual, the support mobilized by the helper may prove insufficient. In this event there should be no undue delay in seeking medical or psychiatric aid as an urgent measure.

So far in this book emphasis has been laid on the intervention in crisis situations by helpers who are not well-trained in psychological or psychiatric techniques. But it should not be thought that the methods and insights of crisis theory and crisis intervention are of small moment to the trained therapist or irrelevant to his concepts and practices. Quite the contrary. Crisis theory is well rooted in psychoanalytic concepts; and it uses these together with knowledge derived from social sciences to formulate a psychosocial approach to patient care that appeals to many well-qualified and experienced psychotherapists. Short-term treatment is no longer simply a matter of necessity or expediency; it may be the method of choice in certain instances. Crisis theory describes the dynamics of change under conditions of stress, brings a new view of the 'precipitating event' and the client's presenting need, and emphasizes the forces outside the individual which may determine the outcome of the crisis. Knowledge such as this enriches the understanding and enhances the capabilities of any therapist.

CHAPTER 4

CRISIS IN THE HOME: CHILD ABUSE

THE health visitor, Miss Brown, had seen the family several times since they moved into their new home in the district. The wife, Mrs. McKay, was a young, pretty, and likeable woman, if at times rather feckless and untidy in her person and habits. She seemed to be harassed always and never quite on top of her household duties. She had three young children and a husband on night-shift. They had recently moved into a council house from a damp, cramped, and expensive flat, largely through the efforts of the local authority social worker, Mrs. Jones.

Mrs. Jones, on her part, had become involved with the family at an earlier stage of their history. At that time Mr. McKay had been injured in an accident, lost his job, and — being overdue with the rent — was being threatened with eviction. At the same time Mrs. McKay was looking forward to having her third child, but had become run-down and dispirited. The family doctor prescribed tonics, but she did not improve and was then referred to the local hospital for a psychiatric opinion. There she was diagnosed as suffering from a depressive neurosis and her personality was labelled 'immature'. The depression was clearly reactive to stress, namely, an unsatisfactory home situation, financial difficulties, and a well-advanced pregnancy. She responded quite quickly to the administration of an anti-depressant, help with her household budget, the prospect of employment for her husband, and the chance of re-housing.

Mrs. McKay was 23 years old when her son was born. The other two children were girls, aged 3 years and 18 months. Things went fairly well with the family for a time, but money was tight and, when they moved into their new house, they could not really afford the furnishings they wanted. They took on hire-purchase commitments and Mr. McKay went on night-shift to earn a little more. His wife missed his company in the evenings, and at night often felt scared to be by herself with the children. In addition, they had to be kept quiet through the day while husband tried to sleep. Soon she began to feel out-of-sorts again and made repeated visits to her general practitioner to consult him about her baby. The complaints seemed trivial — mild fevers, spots, or stomach upsets; but the baby did not thrive and cried a lot. This made both her and her husband irritable. Mr. McKay blamed his wife for being such a poor manager, for her inability to keep the children quiet, and for her loss of interest in their sexual relationship. He started to drink and stay out 'with the lads'. The family doctor was not unaware that things were going badly for the McKay family. He therefore arranged that Miss Brown, the health visitor attached to his practice, should visit the home.

Miss Brown was not happy at the family situation she found. It was evident that Mrs. McKay had more on her plate than she could manage. She missed her husband's sympathy and help and she had no relatives at hand to whom she could turn. The two young daughters appeared healthy, but the baby boy was thin, listless, and often crying. He did not seem responsive when Miss Brown tried to gain his attention or to play with him. Clearly Mrs. McKay had lost interest in her own appearance and in caring for her home. She had become a nagging wife and consequently saw less and less of her husband. One day Miss Brown noticed the baby had bruises over its face which Mrs. McKay explained had been caused by a fall from his high-chair. A week later, the family doctor had a telephone call from the accident and emergency department of the local children's hospital where the baby had been taken with a broken arm. The casualty medical officer said he had suspicions that this was a 'battered baby' and what should they do.

When Miss Brown first heard this news she was quite incredulous; but then she began to piece things together in her mind – Mrs. McKay's irritability, the disruption in the marriage relationship, the baby's bruises and excessive crying. After a short discussion, the general practitioner agreed that baby McKay should be admitted to hospital forthwith for full examination and in-patient care. A meeting was then arranged to include the general practitioner, health visitor, psychiatrist, social worker, and the paediatrician to whose ward the baby had been admitted, in order to decide how to deal further with the crisis. In the event, the family doctor was summoned to deal with another emergency, but the others met and talked the matter over. The paediatrician thought that the police should be informed, but the rest felt that this might destroy the McKay's confidence in them and render the task of helping the family even more difficult. The paediatrician pointed out that the broken arm was not the only injury the baby had suffered. Radiological examination had shown signs of other, older bony injury which had not come to attention at the time. But he agreed that, while the safety and future health of the child was paramount, rehabilitation of the whole family was the goal for which they should strive. After discussion, it was arranged that the psychiatrist and the health visitor should visit the home together and explore the situation. At this point in time it was not clear which of the parents had actually inflicted the injuries.

When Mr. and Mrs. McKay were seen together at home, it was obvious that things were going badly with them. The house was extremely untidy with piles of unwashed dishes in the kitchen and heaps of clothes lying about the living-room. Mr. McKay was uncommunicative and his wife in a state of agitation and distress. It took time and patience before their story was unfolded and enough information pieced together to make possible a future plan of action. The facts that emerged were as follows.

Mr. McKay had been born and brought up in Glasgow. His childhood had not been a happy one. He was one of a large family living in a poor neighbourhood. Father was a shipyard worker who was a stern disciplinarian and also given to hard week-end drinking. He frequently offered physical violence towards his wife and children, particularly when under the influence of alcohol. Young McKay left home at the earliest opportunity, taking himself to London to seek his fortune. There he met a pretty girl in a dance-hall. They fell in love and married with the first child already conceived. In fact, Mrs. McKay was never very keen on the physical side of their marriage, but life went along well enough until Mr. McKay's accident, their financial difficulties, and Mrs. McKay's depression.

As already mentioned, after their third child was born, Mr. McKay went on night-shift. He found sleeping through the day difficult and he became impatient with wife and children. The baby was fractious and Mrs. McKay seemed to find three children more than she could cope with. Their sexual relationship ceased altogether. He started to drink excessively, although he could not afford to; and he met another woman and started an affair with her. His wife got to hear of this liaison, became upset, and nagged him even more. He felt guilty over his own conduct, slept poorly, and found himself losing his temper over trifles. He often rose from bed to chastise the children for the noise they were making. He had always been inclined to make his point by slapping them if they seemed heedless, but on several occasions he alarmed himself by his own loss of control when he found himself shaking or punching one of them in a violent temper. His baby son in particular, of whom he was very fond and proud, roused his anger by crying and screaming. The bruises and the broken arm were inflicted by him when his wife was out shopping. On discovering the injury to the baby's arm, Mrs. McKay had defied him by taking the child to the Casualty Department, but she refused to tell the doctor there what had really occurred. It had all become too much for her and, being of a rather vulnerable personality and not too well endowed with intelligence, she felt more and more that she could not cope with all the difficulties life was heaping upon her. By the time of the visit of psychiatrist and health visitor, she was in a state of acute anxiety and depression. It was decided that she needed more help than could be mustered at home and her admission to a psychiatric unit was arranged. At the same time her other two children were taken into the care of the local authority social work department.

It was anticipated that Mrs. McKay and the baby would both be fit for discharge within a matter of weeks. A number of questions then had to be answered regarding the future of this family. The queries were of a medical, social, and legal nature. Should the police be involved after all and Mr. McKay be charged? Should every effort be made to bring the family together again and help them achieve stability and more satisfying relationships? If so, what about the risk of further injury to the children? Besides all that, were there lessons to be learned from the experience? Could the crisis have been foreseen and prevented? For example, if social worker or health visitor had been able to gain Mrs. McKay's confidence and trust to a greater degree, or if the family doctor had discerned the underlying cause of anxiety when Mrs. McKay brought him the baby with so many apparently trivial complaints, would intervention at these earlier points in time have prevented further disturbance and harm? These questions had (and indeed have) no unequivocal answers. Similar situations occur, but each must be considered in the light of its own circumstances. Nevertheless, certain general observations and guide-lines are discernable and can be stated.

Child abuse, non-accidental injury, or the battered baby syndrome, as it is variously termed, is now accepted to be a major problem. Its recognition, investigation, and treatment may present considerable difficulties and involve doctors, social workers, police, and other workers such as those employed by the Royal Society for Prevention of Cruelty to Children. The injuries inflicted on the child may take a number of different forms and not all of them are likely to arouse suspicion. Fractures of skull, of limb bones, or of ribs may occur; there may be bruises, burns, or swellings; less obvious damage can be suffered by internal organs as a result of blows or because of vigorous shaking. Besides these, there may occur deprivation of food and fluids, anaemia resulting from poor nutrition, or poisoning. The latter may be a consequence of the deliberate administration of toxic substances or by the 'accidental' leaving of them within reach. In addition, there are the more subtle but lasting effects of lack of tender love and consistent caring on the infant's emotional and personality development.

Records indicate that most victims of such behaviour are under the age of 4 years; many are under 2. It cannot be stated with certainty how common such assaults are. Given all the scolding and physical chastisement of children that occurs, it has been suggested that many ordinary parents are potential child-beaters. A figure of some 5000 cases a year has been suggested for the United Kingdom. Another estimate is six children per 1000 live births. The diagnosis is easy to overlook and often difficult to prove even when suspicion has been aroused. Undue delay between the time of the injury and the visit to doctor may be a clue and merit further enquiry. The parents' account of the accident may not fit the physical findings. The emotional attitude of the parents may appear strange or inappropriate; and their account of the child's behaviour may take the form of exaggerated complaint. A history of previous injury or the signs of injuries at different stages of healing must raise deep suspicion.

It is suggested that perhaps as many as half of the parents involved in such behaviour suffered themselves as children from abuse and cruelty. Some workers argue that the proportion is higher and that, in most cases, parents who injure their children are recreating their own pattern and experience of rearing. Often such parents seem to demand of their children a submissive and total obedience to standards which they sanction by an ever-present threat of physical violence. A parent of this kind, who has lacked in his own upbringing a warm or cherishing relationship, may possess quite unrealistic expectations of his own child. He may demand for his own satisfaction from a tiny and uncomprehending human-being that it should never cry, or soil, or be messy at table. In such circumstances, frustration and anger are inevitable; they build up and may be released in a burst of temper, in an attempt at discipline that goes too far, or in a state of alcoholic over-indulgence. A small number of 'battering' parents are identifiably mentally ill and a greater proportion fall into the category of sociopathic personalities. But by far the majority seem to be normal parents who are under stress — for example, a mother worn out by the incessant demands of young children, or a father with just too many problems in his marriage or finances. The parents involved come from all social classes and income groups and there is no clearly demonstrated relationship with low intelligence or poor education. But it does seem likely that a middle-class or well-educated mother will find some outlet or manoeuvre to ease the situation, for example, employing a nanny, or sending a child to play-school, outlets that may be unavailable to the less privileged.

It seems not at all unlikely that many mothers and fathers are ill-prepared for parenthood. Perhaps it is largely mythical that mothering comes naturally. But television advertisements and glossy magazines give substance to the myth by their pictures of beautifully cared-for babies gratefully accepting the effortless love of those around them, helped of course by the product advertised. Women who are not bathed in the incessant glow of satisfied motherhood may be dogged by guilt and may even feel abnormal. Perhaps our society is beginning to realize that we need to educate our young not only for satisfying sex but also for satisfactory parenthood.

Recent reports reveal that children who have been returned to their homes after treatment for non-accidental injury have, all too often, met with further injury and even death. The much publicized case of Maria Colwell (who was beaten to death by her stepfather) highlights some of the difficulties of assessment and the errors of judgment which may be made by competent professional workers. A clear lesson from Maria's unfortunate death is the dire consequences which may follow a failure of communication between different agencies or departments. Decisions taken on inadequate data run the risk of being dangerously mistaken. Even when full information is available, the decision to return the child to its parents may bristle with doubts and difficulties. In some instances the child's interests must over-ride what has tended to be considered in the past the 'natural rights' of parents. It is unreasonable, however, that such dilemmas be left for isolated or inexperienced social workers to solve. Instead there might be established in each hospital region a specialised team comprising paediatrician, psychiatrist, and social worker. They could carry out an assessment, seeking information from others involved, such as G.P. or R.S.P.C.C., and reach a joint decision that would safeguard the child's health and development. In this way not only would decision-making be shared, but also the team's expertise would grow as they accumulated experience.

On the basis of recent studies, it is suggested that particular caution should be exercised in returning a baby to a home where one or other parent demonstrates a grossly abnormal personality, is of subnormal intelligence, or is known to have a criminal record. But it is very much part of the problem that no rigid criteria can be laid down. Consequently it may be equally well argued that the care and support of skilled helpers, who can alleviate distressful living conditions and encourage social re-learning, may transform an unsuitable family setting into one where the return of the child can be safely contemplated.

In the case of the McKay family, it seemed that both parents were within the range of normality, although Mr. McKay had experienced a somewhat affectionless childhood and Mrs. McKay tended to respond to stress with symptoms of depression and anxiety. But neither of them were so disturbed in personality as would preclude a stable marital relationship. Given Mrs. McKay's return to normal health, their real affection for one another, and some intelligent reappraisal and alteration of circumstances (for example, Mr. McKay's return to day-shift) it appeared possible that this family could be reconstituted. At a further conference of those involved, when Mrs. McKay's improvement in the psychiatric unit heralded her early discharge, it was agreed that the two eldest children should be returned home. Miss Brown, the health visitor, undertook to visit the family regularly and had already made a point of visiting Mrs. McKay in hospital. Besides this, the psychiatrist intended to arrange to see the couple, together with Miss Brown, in marital therapy for a time. Depending on the progress achieved and a careful weighing of the relevent circumstances, baby McKay would be returned home also or retained for a longer period in the care of the social services department. It was generally agreed that, now that the acute emergency was over, the essence of rehabilitation was for the health visitor to establish and maintain a trusted and supporting relationship over a lengthy period. The other agencies and resources already involved would be available for support and consultation.

CHAPTER 5

CRISIS IN THE HOME : MARITAL STRIFE

MR. FLYNN, probation officer, was asked by the Court to provide a social background report on Mr. James Kennedy, aged 22 years, who had been charged with causing a disturbance in a neighbour's house and being drunk and disorderly. Mr. Flynn called at their home to see both Mr. and Mrs. Kennedy.

Jim Kennedy was a slim, good-looking young man who talked about himself readily enough. His wife, a few years older than himself, was sharp-featured and seemed tense. There were two young children aged 2 and 4. The house was tidy and comfortable and Mr. Flynn was offered a cup of tea. Mrs. Kennedy did most of the talking at first, saying how difficult things were since Jim stopped work and she complained about his drinking. She had taken a part-time job to help financially but was finding life a strain, Her husband was moody and unpredictable in his behaviour. He was often irritable and bad-tempered with her and the children and sometimes, she felt, he was not really well. She had nagged him into consulting his general practitioner, Dr. Wilson, who had prescribed some pills and these had helped somewhat. 'Dr. Wilson's a bit fed-up with me, I think,' said Mr. Kennedy at this point, 'because I haven't been very co-operative with him I suppose.' Mr. Flynn obtained the following account and prepared a report for the Court.

Jim Kennedy was born of respectable working-class parents. He was the only son in a family of four. He got on well at home and was particularly fond of his mother. At school he achieved a moderate success, but left as soon as he could to earn money. This was the beginning of a chequered career. He was employed first as a van boy, but became bored with it and decided to join the Army as a boy entrant. He ran away after 1 month and, brought back to his unit, repeated this behaviour on three further occasions. He persuaded his father to buy him out, pleading homesickness and that he missed his girl-friend Mabel who was a friend from schooldays and a year younger than himself. He began work in a local factory but disliked the shifts and left after 2 weeks. This resulted in a row with his father. He then announced he had found a new and better job and set out each morning as if to go to work. But

34

there was, in fact, no job, When this was discovered, he disappeared from home taking with him Mabel and £10 stolen from his mother. The girl's mother informed the police of her daughter's disappearance and, after a few days, both runaways were apprehended in Birmingham. Jim was charged with theft and also with having unlawful carnal knowledge of a girl under sixteen. He was placed on probation for 2 years. But soon afterwards he committed a housebreaking and was sent to Borstal. While he was there, Mabel discovered she was pregnant, and much to Jim's annoyance, an abortion was arranged. On his discharge he refused to have anything more to do with Mabel. He found a job and a new girl-friend, Betty, whom he married soon after. He was then only 18 and his wife 22. Their marriage was stormy from the start. Jim had started drinking heavily, he lost several jobs because of this, and he and his wife quarrelled frequently over his failure (as she put it) to accept the responsibilities of husband and father. He struck her several times when under the influence of alcohol and on one occasion broke her nose. Their family doctor, Dr. Wilson, and his health visitor were frequently involved — called in to deal with Mrs. Kennedy's 'nerves' or Mr. Kennedy's 'depression', which at other times presented as gastritis or severe headaches. Dr. Wilson had arranged several appointments for Jim with the psychiatrist but he either did not attend or refused to co-operate with any treatment plans. Mrs. Kennedy had left him on several occasions, taking the two children to live with her mother; but Jim was contrite and persuaded her each time to return.

The row with the neighbour, Mr. Brown, occurred after they had been out drinking together. They took some beer and whisky back to Mr. Brown's house and continued drinking until both were quite intoxicated. Jim did not recall clearly what had happened, but remembered an argument about the local football team. This escalated into a fight and furniture was smashed and thrown about. Mrs. Brown became alarmed and telephoned the police who arrested Jim and later charged him.

Mr. Flynn pondered over this story, talking to Dr. Wilson by telephone, and decided to recommend to the Court that Jim Kennedy be put on probation once more. He found something appealing about Jim, despite his irresponsible behaviour, and felt he could help him and his family. The Court agreed and Mr. Flynn was appointed probation officer with the task of befriending and advising Mr. James Kennedy. As the magistrate made the order, Mr. Flynn could not but recall Dr. Wilson's pessimistic prognostications and his firmly expressed opinion that Kennedy deserved the label of 'psychopath'.

Two weeks after the Court had made the probation order, the police received a telephone call from Mrs. Kennedy. It was just before midnight and she sounded tearful and agitated. She said her husband had been drinking, had returned home in an ugly mood, and was sitting in the kitchen with a carving knife affirming his intention of killing her and then himself. The duty Inspector tried to reassure Mrs. Kennedy and arranged for a police officer to go to the house immediately. There he found Mr. Kennedy sitting, as his wife had described, holding a carving-knife, and refusing to answer questions. The officer reported the situation to his Inspector who happened to know Jim Kennedy's history and his involvement with Mr. Flynn. He decided to call Mr. Flynn who agreed to visit the Kennedy home forthwith.

A little apprehensively, Mr. Flynn decided to sit down with Jim on his own and try to understand the situation more clearly. At first, Jim paid him no heed, did not even acknowledge his presence, and made no reply to questions. Mr. Flynn continued to talk quietly to him nevertheless and Jim suddenly threw down the knife and burst into tears. Thereafter in a disjointed fashion, and with much sobbing and some shouting, Jim Kennedy expressed his feelings of guilt and despair. He talked of his mother's death 2 years previously and how much he missed her; he said how often he thought of his old girl-friend Mabel and how badly he had treated her; he knew he was unfair to his wife and children and should find a job and control his drinking, but his good intentions seemed to crumble; he got moods when he hated everybody, including himself, and often thought he would be better off dead. At such times he set off to get drunk and insensible. As he talked he gradually became calmer and more rational. Mr. Flynn assured Mrs. Kennedy and the police officer that things were now under control and promised Jim that he was pre-pared to help him further. They arranged to meet the following morning at Mr. Flynn's office. Jim did not come. On visiting the home, Mr. Flynn learned that Jim had left that morning with the apparent intention of keeping the ap-pointment. His wife expressed concern and anger that he had not done so and said that no doubt he was off drinking again.

Next day Mr. Flynn was telephoned by Dr. Wilson who said that the health visitor was very concerned about the Kennedys. In particular Mrs. Kennedy was coming to the end of her tether and was also in financial difficulties. Could Mr. Flynn help further? Should they arrange for Jim to see a psychia-trist? After some discussion of the current problems, it was agreed that Dr. Wilson should arrange for Jim to be seen as an out-patient at the psychiatric clinic. However, before the appointment day arrived, Jim Kennedy was ad-mitted to the casualty department of the local hospital after taking an overdose of his wife's sleeping pills. He was seen there by a psychiatrist and, at his own request was admitted to the psychiatric hospital for treatment of his alcoholism and depression.

While recognizing the limits set on their endeavours by the patient's past history and the sociopathic nature of his personality, the psychiatric treatment team decided to give Jim Kennedy the benefit of the doubt. After a short spell as an in-patient, Jim attended as a day-patient and was treated in a therapeutic community setting with emphasis on group therapy and family involvement. Mr. Flynn also agreed to be involved and took part with the psychiatrist in regular marital therapy sessions with the Kennedys. This intensive treatment situation extended over 3 months and contact was maintained thereafter on an out-patient basis, Jim having returned to full employment. During his treatment in the day hospital several crises arose. For example, Jim became enamoured of a young woman patient who reminded him of Mabel and talked at one point of leaving his wife so that they could go off together. However, the situation was openly discussed by the patients and staff together, Mrs. Kennedy was supported during this episode, and the unrealistic nature of the infatuation became apparent to both patients. In addition there was more than one episode when Jim resorted to alcohol in the face of situational stress and he physically assaulted his wife during one such bout. Sometimes he failed to attend treatment sessions and on one occasion had to be readmitted to an emergency bed for 2 days, threatening suicide. On many occasions the psychiatric staff felt angry and frustrated; but over the weeks progress was made and became apparent not only to them but also to Mr. Flynn, Dr. Wilson, the health visitor, and the Kennedys themselves. After a year the family had apparently reached a large measure of stability. Jim was working regularly and not drinking. Mrs. Kennedy was happier and no longer under stress. Their relationship was closer than it had ever been before.

Are there lessons to be learned from this account? Insofar as intervention in this case was successful, what helped to make it so?

1. One factor of great importance was Mr. Flynn's commitment to the family and, in particular, his sympathetic acceptance of Jim Kennedy. It is possible to make minor criticisms of the probation officers' handling of the case, for example, that he might have been quicker to recognize the serious nature of Kennedy's mental state and consulted the psychiatric services sooner. But his willingness to respond to his client's appeals, and to see beyond the acting-out behaviour to the less obvious

feelings of inadequacy and guilt, were crucial in maintaining contact and eventually bringing Jim face-to-face with himself. When 'tested-out' by Jim, Mr. Flynn was able to respond without rejecting his client. His commitment extended to following Jim into treatment in the psychiatric clinic and taking part regularly in marital therapy.

2. This emphasizes the second factor of importance in this case. There was a considerable effort on the part of all concerned to communicate and share in the decision-making regarding the Kennedys. More might have been done in this way; but the effort was sufficient to ensure that agencies were working together and not pulling in different directions.

3. A third factor of importance was Jim's treatment in a therapeutic community. Perhaps the situation was ripe for therapeutic intervention of any kind; perhaps Jim was beginning to 'grow up' and accept responsibility in any case. On the other hand, the culture of the day hospital in which he was treated was able to accept and contain him — even through his crises of misbehaviour — in a way which a more traditional regime might not. The on-going support and confrontation by staff and fellow-patients enabled his behaviour and feelings to be examined and their origins elucidated. In such a situation it was possible for him to be faced repeatedly with his evasions and derelictions, his flight into alcohol, and how all this might be abandoned for behaviour which was more constructive and fulfilling. His progress towards understanding, control, and responsibility was helped considerably by his wife's willingness to join in treatment with him and examine their relationship together. It was possible in marital therapy to open up communication between the pair and work through some of Jim's 'hang-ups'.

All this, it is true, goes well beyond the ordinary conception of crisis intervention. But it is important to be aware that sticking a finger into any crisis situation brings some responsibility for the further outcome. In many cases it will be sensible and necessary to withdraw once the immediate crisis is resolved. In other instances, the client may have to be referred to another agency. In this particular case of a family in trouble, centering round the personality disorder of Jim Kennedy, Mr. Flynn took the view that his professional commitment gave him a continuing role in Jim's treatment. There is no doubt that it paid off for all concerned.

CHAPTER 6

CRISIS IN THE HOME : OLD AGE

MISS Wood's neighbours finally decided to call the police. They had not seen her for several days and loud and repeated knocking at her door aroused no response. Two policemen drove up quickly and asked questions. They were told that Miss Wood was in her seventies and had not seemed so well in the past few weeks. But no one saw much of her as she tended to avoid her neighbours. Lately she had been quite odd at times, appearing forgetful, muddled, and even aggressive. She had no visitors. Such members of her family as they knew about lived abroad. The only person coming regularly to the house was her general practitioner, Dr. Munro. His health visitor used to call quite often at one time, but not for some months. The church minister too visited regularly until his retirement a year ago, when Miss Wood refused to have any dealings with his successor.

The police officers were faced with a solid front door leading to an upstairs flat. There was no answer to their knocking or when they shouted through the letter-box. The windows at the back were securely fastened, but they noticed that the bedroom window, in front, was open. A ladder was borrowed from a neighbour and the sergeant managed to crawl through. He found Miss Wood lying in bed and thought at first she might be dead. But breathing was evident and she seemed to be comatose. Dr. Munro was called, examined Miss Wood briefly, thought she probably had pneumonia, and summoned an ambulance to transfer her to hospital.

Both the sergeant and the doctor were taken aback at the state of the flat. In the first place it was crowded with furniture; but in addition objects of all kinds — ornaments, pictures, books, articles of clothing, and crockery — lay all around. Bundles of old newspapers and magazines heaped the floor, were piled upon chairs, and were stuffed under bed and table. Everything seemed dusty. They peered into the small kitchen and found it in chaos, full of unwashed dishes, greasy pots, half-empty tins, and residues of food. The bed and bedclothes Miss Wood had been using were damp and soiled.

Under treatment in hospital Miss Wood improved quickly. She seemed a cheerful old lady and, although somewhat frail, was soon insisting on being up and moving about the ward. She revealed an independence of spirit, liked doing things for herself, and was humorously critical of nurses and doctors in quite an outspoken way. She announced her intention of returning home but, having heard of the state of her flat and that she lived alone, the physician was not willing to discharge her. In addition he had some doubts about her mental state and so decided to ask for a psychiatric opinion.

Miss Wood talked to the psychiatrist at length, although not always to the point. Once or twice she broke off her account to make a critical comment about ward staff or fellow-patients. She had considerable difficulty with times and dates, appearing much more confident when talking about remote rather than recent events. Indeed her memory for recent events seemed poor and she became irritated with the psychiatrist when he asked her questions to test it. He talked instead of her life at home and Miss Wood told how well things had gone when she and her mother had lived together. But her mother had died 18 years ago and she missed her company and support. In recent years she had not enjoyed good health. She suffered from high blood-pressure, arthritis, and mild diabetes. From time to time she also developed urinary infections for which Dr. Munro gave her pills. These were effective; but while the symptoms lasted they were very troublesome because her lavatory was outside the house and she had difficulty negotiating stairs. She had tried to exchange to a downstairs flat and had also applied for one of the small flats for old folk the council had built. But there was a long waiting-list and no immediate prospect for her. She went down the street most days for her shopping, collected her pension regularly from the Post Office, sometimes talked to the milkman, and otherwise saw only her doctor whose surgery she visited frequently for prescriptions for her many ailments.

In the circumstances the psychiatrist thought it wise to transfer Miss Wood to the psychiatric unit for fuller assessment. She took some time to persuade, insisting that she was quite well and that she wished to go home. But finally she agreed. The psychiatrist also wanted time to investigate Miss Wood's domestic situation a little more fully and he asked the social worker attached to his unit to visit the town, some 20 miles distant, where the patient lived. The social worker obtained Miss Wood's consent and the key to her flat. She confirmed the dirty and neglected state of the house, had a word with the next-door neighbour, and visited the general practitioner. Dr. Munro himself was fairly elderly and had known Miss Wood for many years. He thought she had never been the same after her mother died. She had become solitary and a little suspicious of people, living the life almost of a recluse. At the same time she had been quite vigorous and independent until recently. Her physical disabilities had become burdensome and he felt her memory was failing. Shopkeepers had told him Miss Wood could not remember sometimes what she had come to buy, and she got in a muddle over prices and her change. The health visitor attached to his practice used to visit Miss Wood regularly. When she left to get married, Miss Wood refused to have her successor call on her. Also, when Dr. Munro had arranged for a home-help a month or two ago, Miss Wood quarrelled with her and the home-help refused to return. The doctor had been aware for several months that Miss Wood was deteriorating, both physically and mentally, ('We are none of us getting any younger', he joked to the social worker) and he had noticed she had become rather neglectful of her house. However, he had been quite unprepared for the chaotic state he had found it in on Miss Wood's transfer to hospital. He presumed the hospital would be retaining Miss Wood or arranging her admission to a geriatric or psychiatric ward. The social worker explained they were investigating the situation further, but that Miss Wood was very keen to come home again.

The investigations, physical and psychological, carried out on Miss Wood revealed the truth of her own statements that she was somewhat hypertensive, had osteo-arthritis – particularly in her hips, and suffered from a mild degree of diabetes. There was some hardening of her arteries and evidence of a dementing process. That is, there was a disturbance of brain function, with some impairment of her intellectual functions particularly memory, and also effects on general behaviour. This so-called 'dementia' had been present, in all probability, for some years, but Miss Wood's restricted and organized existence prevented any obvious symptoms. More recently her memory disturbance, neglect of her household tasks, and her odd and irritable behaviour were evident signs of the disturbance. The crisis provided by her pneumonia brought the whole matter to light. Her stay in hospital had improved her general physical condition and, although she was still handicapped, she expressed a keen desire to return home. The staff discussed the prospect at some length. It was finally decided to give her the chance. There would need to be conscientious follow-up and support for her and something needed to be done as soon as possible about her flat.

The social worker contacted the social work department of the town in which Miss Wood lived. She explained the situation and arrangements were made for a home-help from that department together with a small group of volunteer university students to engage in 'operation clear-up' in Miss Wood's flat. This took several visits; on the final one the social worker took Miss

Wood with her to agree about what might be thrown out and what retained. One surprise for the social worker was to find a drawer in Miss Wood's dressing-table packed with medicines. There were bottles and boxes of various kinds and she recognized analgesics, antibiotics, and hypnotics, as well as many other pills and capsules with which she was unfamiliar. She wondered how Miss Wood had remembered which was which, or how many to take and when. On asking Miss Wood about this, she found the latter quite vague about it all. She confiscated the lot and later reported the problem to the psychiatrist. He talked to Dr. Munro and it was agreed that Miss Wood's medication would be kept as simple as possible and supervised as far as that could be arranged. A few days later, a psychiatric nurse, who had got to know Miss Wood well in the ward, accompanied her home, helped her to do some necessary shopping, and saw her settled in. A little excited, Miss Wood was happy to be back in her familiar surroundings. Arrangements had been made for regular visits from the local authority social work department, Dr. Munro, and also a home-help several days a week.

Things went well for several weeks. However, it then became increasingly apparent that difficulties were emerging. Miss Wood again quarrelled with the home-help who, she felt, was refusing to do things her way. The neighbours, who had been friendly enough before, appeared less so. They clearly had not anticipated Miss Wood's return from hospital and resented the presence of a 'crazy old lady' in the same building or next door to them. The local social worker telephoned the psychiatrist to say that she and Dr. Munro felt that Miss Wood was managing only at a precarious level and sometimes appeared confused. Dr. Munro suggested to Miss Wood that he might arrange to find accommodation for her in the old folks home, but she became very annoyed at this and insisted she was perfectly capable of managing where she was.

About a month later a further crisis occurred. Miss Wood accidentally set fire to her living-room. It was her custom to bank up the coal-fire in this room to keep it burning economically. The hot coals had fallen on the carpet while she lay asleep in the armchair and a blaze was underway before she woke and gave the alarm. She was shocked and had minor burns to her legs, necessitating admission to hospital. Her mental and physical state deteriorated after this, she became a patient in a psychogeriatric ward, and her house was given up.

Comment

This case-history illustrates a number of general points. Mental disturbance is common in old people and impairment of general mental ability is a frequent accompaniment to ageing. Moreover the proportion of the elderly in our population is increasing. In Britain they account for over twelve per cent of the total population, are said to utilize thirty per cent of the National Health Service budget, and occupy a high proportion of hospital beds. The condition labelled 'dementia' is common. About 10 per cent of old people are said to be demented and in the over-eighties, this number rises to more than one in five.[12] Among the very old, women outnumber men by more than two to one, so there are more demented women than men. As the number of old people increases, the problem of their care and treatment becomes more urgent. Some impression of the size of the present problem can be gained from the survey of Kay and his colleagues[13] in Newcastle, where 41 per cent of elderly people living at home were found to have psychiatric abnormality; the survey conducted by Williamson[14] in Edinburgh suggested 55 per cent as the likely figure. As the Millar Report[15] points out: 'Mental disorder is sometimes easily identified – as in major crises such as impulsive behaviour and suicide; sometimes wrongly identified – for example when emotional conditions are thought to be physical illnesses; and sometimes not identified at all. This iceberg phenomenon is perhaps most evident among the elderly where natural reserve, physical isolation and "covering up" by relatives conspire to obscure the picture'. The likelihood is that there is much emotional disorder among old people in the community which is undetected and yet susceptible to prevention or alleviation.

Doctors find the care of the elderly a taxing problem, both in and out of hospital. The list of an average general practitioner contains thirty to forty demented patients.[12] They make a disproportionate demand on his attention, not least because their problems often present as crises. This may be because the care and treatment facilities for the old do not match the demand, and preventive measures fall far short of what is necessary. The day is fast approaching when the elderly will be the main consumers of hospital services and residential care. It is thus of considerable importance that they are maintained in the community as long as possible. This means wide-ranging personal social services, a generous policy with regard to old-age pensions, more sheltered housing, and a greater availability of residential care. The old person requiring long-stay accommodation may be physically disabled, mentally disturbed, and often is both. It is this combination which seems to provide difficulty.

In past times, the medical profession took a pessimistic view of the illnesses of old age. Many patients were consigned to mental hospitals or chronic sick wards with conditions which in fact were remediable given more skilful assessment and better treatment facilities. However, the recent and welcome growth of psycho-geriatric assessment and treatment centres and the proliferation of day-care demonstrate an increasing awareness of these problems and a willingness to deal with them.

It may still be true that many doctors and social workers, faced with a disturbed old person, feel that the immediate solution is to get him or her into hospital. In some cases this may be the correct and inevitable disposal. But the issue of hospitalization turns largely on the resources available in family and community. As in the case of Miss Wood, the biggest difficulty is provided by the old person living alone, since round-the-clock care is seldom to be had. Hospital becomes the only answer, not because of the need for fuller investigation or skilled nursing, but simply because it may be the one situation where continuous supervision is possible. In other circumstances, where an aged relative is being cared for in a devoted family setting, it may become clear that the relatives are being stressed beyond their reasonable capacity. Doctor or social worker may then have to persuade the family of the necessity for institutional care and help them subsequently with their mixed feelings of guilt and relief.

In 1961 the Allan Report[16] affirmed: 'The object of every local authority must be to expand their mental health services to the point at which no person need be resident in hospital unless he will benefit from or requires hospital care.' The 1962 Hospital Plan for England and Wales[17] emphasized the need for all types of community care for those not requiring hospital treatment. Unfortunately there are few areas in Britain where such obligations are within reach of fulfilment. As far as elderly patients are concerned, many are admitted to hospital for social rather than medical reasons and others cannot be discharged because there is no accommodation in residential homes or domiciliary support is inadequate. Among its many recommendations the Millar Report emphasizes the need for greater community support of the elderly. It cites the usefulness of an 'at risk register' for the general practitioner, who is in a position to co-ordinate the various agencies involved. These include health visitors who might be more fully trained and utilized in dealing with mental disorder in the elderly; a home-nursing and night-sitter service to be called upon in an emergency; domiciliary visiting in such matters as chiropody, deaf-aids, and physiotherapy; more imaginative home-help and provision of meals; increased day-centre facilities with suitable transport arrangements; and greater encouragement and co-ordination of voluntary workers.

Had such resources been available in Miss Wood's case, it seems unlikely that the crises described would have arisen. At least her difficulties would have been dealt with at an earlier stage and she might well have been enabled to spend further years of more fulfilled life in her own community.

CHAPTER 7

CRISIS OF BEREAVEMENT

GRIEF results when a love tie is severed. The loss of husband or wife is a severe stress and yet a common one. Death and dying nevertheless have become taboo subjects in our society and, whereas sexual problems are quite freely discussed, the fears and distress which surround death are generally avoided. The death of a relative or friend reminds us that we are all mortal. Do we live acknowledging this fact or escaping from it? Can we prepare for bereavement and for our own dying? Is it possible to help others to do so?

Considerable knowledge exists about bereavement, its effects upon mental and physical health, and the mixture of emotions which may be engendered. Parkes[18] has written a very useful book on the subject, in which he discusses the various forms grief may assume, the factors which affect its course, and the means by which the outcome of grieving can be modified. Bereavement is a common social crisis which clearly illustrates some of the views expressed in Chapter 3 where Crisis Theory and Crisis Intervention are discussed. It is an occasion of stress when individuals and families are open to help or harm. Those who come into contact with the dying and the bereaved have an opportunity of responding sensitively and constructively. Yet often it seems that the protection, reassurance, and active help which are needed and might be expected from doctors, nurses, clergymen and others is given ineptly, without understanding, or not at all.

It is only in recent years that psychiatrists have paid much attention to grief or 'the loss complex' as it is sometimes called. The relationship between mourning and depressive illness was pointed out by Freud[19] and later discussed by other pyscho-analysts. Perhaps the first real consideration of grief as a recognizable clinical entity was provided by the work of Lindemann.[20,21] He investigated the reactions of the bereaved survivors of the Cocoanut Grove fire in Boston and later made other observations of bereavement (e.g. in the families of servicemen) from which he arrived at four main conclusions. They may be summarized as follows:

1. Acute grief is a definite syndrome with psychological and physical

symptoms.

2. This syndrome may appear immediately following the crisis or it may be delayed.
3. Distorted reactions may take the place of the typical syndrome; symptoms may be exaggerated, highlight one particular aspect of the loss, or may be apparently absent altogether.
4. By use of appropriate helping measures, a distorted reaction may be transformed into normal grieving and the individual guided towards a successful solution of the crisis.

Grief results not only from the death of someone close, but also may be the consequence of a broken relationship (e.g. divorce), loss of employment, the loss of part of the body (e.g. amputation of a limb), or the destruction of a highly valued ideal. So grief may be defined as the emotional and physical reaction to any important personal loss. It is in fact normal and appropriate in such circumstances. Grieving, if completed successfully, brings psychological acceptance of the loss and the restoration of emotional equilibrium. In some ways grief bears a close resemblance to physical injury; for example, the loss is spoken of as a blow or a wound. As in physical hurt, the wound is expected to heal gradually; but occasionally complications supervene – healing is delayed, or a further injury reopens the wound. In this fashion, grief may be viewed as an illness or at least as a process which involves a succession of clinical states. And just as a broken bone may end up stronger than it was originally, so the experience of grieving may bring strength and maturity to the personality. The pain of grief, suggests Parkes, is just as much a part of life as the joy of love. Indeed it may be the price we pay for love – the cost of our mutual commitment. To ignore this fact is to wear emotional blinkers and leave ourselves unprepared for the inevitable wounds and losses that occur in our own lives and in the lives of those we hope to help.

On the other hand, if we are ready to face, and thus help others to face, the loss as it really is, we may have to undergo or share painful emotions. A loss has to be experienced before it can be recovered from. Sadness and pain are part of normal reaction; a flow of tears often betokens the release of pent-up feelings and may be encouraged as part of the healing process. Initial shock and numbness give place to pining which, in turn, becomes depression. These feelings should not be resisted or jollied away. Their working-through may need to be repeated over and over again. This is what is called 'grief-work'. It is the unavoidable task of mourning which, when completed, enables the bereaved individual to get on with his life.

In grieving there is therefore a typical pattern of response, the features of which can be recognized. Each stage of the crisis has its characteristics but there are many variations with regard to form or duration. One basic necessity in grief-work is the recovery by the bereaved person of the emotional investment he made in the lost loved-one; he needs to draw this emotion back into himself, as it were, so that he may have it to reinvest later in another person or another part of his life. In the pain and loneliness of severe loss, the bereaved may think this a remote or unlikely goal. But in the course of time, particularly with support, he can be restored to normal capacity and functioning.

Normal grieving

Lindemann, Parkes, and others have described the clinical picture of normal grief. The physical features of the acute stage generally include feelings of exhaustion and lack of strength, tightness in the throat, choking sensations, a marked tendency to sigh, an awareness of tension, and also digestive symptoms. Individuals complain, 'The slightest effort makes me exhausted'; or 'Food tastes like nothing'. They become aware that symptoms can be precipitated by mention of the dead person or by expressions of sympathy and they avoid social occasions where such talk is to be anticipated.

To a loss which is sudden or severe, the immediate reaction is one of shock and incomprehension. There may be initial denial of the event. As this stage passes, there may occur a mild but pervading sense of unreality and a feeling of emotional distance from others. This is often accompanied by a deep preoccupation with the image of the dead person. Grief is experienced in pangs, that is, feelings of acute distress. At such times the bereaved sobs and cries out for the lost person. Pangs of grief begin shortly after bereavement takes place and tend to reach a peak of severity within the first week or two. Thereafter they occur less frequently and may only be precipitated by chance events which bring the loss to mind, for example, coming across an old snapshot when clearing out a drawer or hearing a favourite song on the radio. Deep preoccupation with the dead person is called pining and seems to be a necessary part of grief-work. There is need to describe the lost person, to recall and search through memories no matter how painful, and try to make sense of what has happened. This searching and yearning may be mixed with, or closely followed by, feelings of guilt and anger. The bereaved accuses himself and others of neglect and negligence. Minor omissions get exaggerated. Feelings of hostility are expressed to relatives and friends, sometimes in loud outbursts, which alarm not only those around but also the person himself. He sometimes concludes he is going out of his mind. Besides this, he may engage in intense but unnecessary routine or in aimless activity. There seems to be a search for something to do, a restless striving to find what cannot be found. It may be an attempt to give pattern and significance to a chaotic situation, a life that has lost its central core and purpose.

Bowlby[22] states that anger is a normal component of grief; and Parkes in his study[23] of London widows found that most of them experienced feelings of anger at some time during the first year of bereavement. This emotion tended to be most noticeable during the first month; it was reported only intermittently thereafter. Between episodes of anger there were periods of apathy, withdrawal and depression. Depression became more prominent as the year passed. This suggests that anger is a feature of the early, yearning phase of grief, whereas the later phase is characterized by feelings of apathy or despair.

A revealing complaint of bereaved people is impairment of the experience of self. For example, they say, 'I feel empty' or 'I feel as if half of me is missing.' These feelings are not surprising when one considers how closely one's sense of identity is bound-up with family relationships. A widow cannot help but be reminded day by day of how large a part of her household activities are now of small consequence, their significance being lost with her dead husband. She lays the table for two instead of one – and then suddenly remembers. 'We' has become 'I'. The present takes on a different pattern; the future assumes a new meaning. Without her life partner, growing old holds a dire significance.

Normal grief reaction therefore includes feelings of shock, physical symptoms, pining, feelings of anger, guilt, and depression, and disturbance of customary patterns of behaviour. The duration of the reaction depends on how successfully the work of mourning is performed. While islands of disturbance may remain for very much longer, most people will reach an equilibrium after a period of months. Much of the earlier reaction is the result of psychological defence mechanisms protecting the bereaved person against the full impact of his loss. Such defences are necessary for survival; but ultimately they are self-defeating if they prevent his acceptance of reality, his emancipation from the dead, and the formation of fresh relationships. The expression of feelings of distress is a part of grief-work and yet, understandably enough, something which many people try to avoid. It is because of this that outside help and guidance may prove vital. A helper or therapist, who has faced his own crisis of misery and done his own grief-work, is in a good position to aid others with theirs.

Particularly 'at risk'

From studies of bereavement it is possible to describe the sort of person who runs a high risk of breakdown. Typically, she is a young widow with small children and no close relatives living near. She is by nature shy and dependent and her relationship to her husband is over-reliant or ambivalent. His death catches her unprepared. She has a previous history of a depressive episode. Her personality and the culture in which she lives discourage open expression of feelings. Since her husband's death she is finding it difficult to bring up the children and financial worries increase the strain. At first, she seems to cope surprisingly well. But then feelings of helplessness and anger start to emerge.

This young woman seems destined for a psychiatric breakdown. Is it worth asking therefore whether anything can be done by way of prevention. The answer is a resounding 'Yes'. But it is a fact that in our society many people face such crises without the help they need. In former times, before our culture became so slick and urbanized, it is likely that formal religious belief and ritual, the community of the Church, and the participation of relatives and friends gave support and guidance. Gorer[24] comments of our present times, 'Mourning is treated as if it were a weakness, a self-indulgence, a reprehensible bad habit instead of a psychological necessity.'

The dying

There is a tradition in medicine that encourages doctors, nurses, and relatives to tell lies to the dying patient. This conviction that the person suffering from a fatal disease should not be told the truth about his condition deserves review. The matter is certainly no simple one. The difficulties are complex, need to be considered carefully in each individual case, and no general rule can be followed. But evidence grows that it may be disadvantageous to all concerned for the patient to be kept in ignorance. Indeed it seems that the reticence of medical and nursing attendants is often a consequence of their own apprehensions rather than of careful assessment of the patient's particular needs. The task of telling a man he is dying may be formidable. It involves painful communication, the need for a caring relationship, and the expenditure of time. But what is the alternative? Should doctor or hospital staff set out on a course of deception, the family of the patient can do little but follow this established pretence. A wife then shoulders the burden not only of caring for a sick husband but also the strain of pretending day after day that all is well. The close relationship which both need to engage in, now more than ever, is denied them. This gives rise to great difficulties at the time; it also prevents the wife from preparing mentally for her loss. She is denied the anticipatory grief which may well render the period of actual bereavement less painful. Moreover, the investigations of Hinton[25] into the reactions of dying patients show that most of them are glad to discuss their fears with a sympathetic listener, particularly one who can share their feelings realistically. Of course it is difficult for busy hospital staff, preoccupied with medical investigations and surgical procedures, committed to the work of curing disease and saving lives, to face the 'failure' of a dying patient. There is 'nothing to be done' they feel. Understandable though this attitude is, it is nevertheless mistaken. If medical and nursing staff can learn to share feelings among themselves as regularly as they communicate information about blood-counts and x-rays, it may be possible for them to be more accepting of death as part of their working lives. It is possible to see death as a meaningful event, one in which all are involved. Ward-staff who can face this together can provide the psychological as well as the physical responses their patients need.

It is probable that in each case the patient's own attitude, if one takes care to listen, gives guidance on what or how much to tell. It may be that, in some cases at least, the patient's own clergyman or the hospital padre can accept a major role in this demanding situation. If frank discussion with the dying patient does seem appropriate and does take place, then it is possible for his wife to share his thoughts and feelings, plan ahead, and look to the future without the flimsy and false protection of lies and bogus optimism.

Helping the bereaved

The newly bereaved person is often in the phase of crisis which, in Chapter 3 was called 'Impact'. A young woman, who has just been informed of her husband's unexpected death, is likely to be in a state of numbness and bewilderment. She will require help with simple household routines and at first may well need to be relieved of such duties as preparing food and looking after the children. In fact she herself will require 'looking after' and this is the most useful task her friends and relatives can perform at this time. The widow may then take the opportunity she needs to begin her own task, that of psychological reorganization. It may be impossible for those around her to gauge her real needs and they may have to fall back on the simple rule of doing nothing to discourage the free expression of feeling. As Parkes[18] points out, physical death and social death do not occur simultaneously. Grieving is the process that fills the gap and it takes time. It is the process of realization, of coming to accept the loss as a fact. Time is an essential element and different members of a bereaved family may need to use it in their own particular ways. Sometimes it seems that the very bonds within a family prevent the full expression of grief. The widow, in our present example, may hold back her intense feelings of distress so as not to upset her children. Or her son may stifle his own alarm to avoid hurting his mother. In such circumstances someone outside the family circle may fulfil a useful role.

Those who have investigated bereavement reactions point out repeatedly how some people are startled by the great intensity of their feelings and imaginings. It is always worth giving reassurance in these cases that strong feelings are natural, that weeping is a normal outlet, and that anger and bitterness are understandable. A widow who complains of feeling unreal, of her lack of concentration, of nightmares, or of fleeting sight and sound of her dead husband may think she is going insane. Clear reassurance that her reactions are within the normal range of experience is worth giving.

On the other hand, where signs of grief are absent or long delayed; where overactivity is combined with an apparent sense of well-being that rings false; where there is a tendency to adopt the style and habits of the deceased or to develop the symptoms that characterized his last illness; or when there is expression of intense guilt or furious hostility; then all these signs should be taken as warnings of a distorted grief reaction. Such a reaction may well be outside the competence of the non-professional who should not hesitate to confide in someone more expert.

Besides relatives, the people usually involved in a bereavement are the general practitioner, clergyman, and funeral undertaker. In the United States it is customary to rely more fully than in Britain on the services of the funeral director who may play quite a significant role in comforting the bereaved. Their more unscrupulous and fanciful practices have been ridiculed by Evelyn Waugh in his novel, *The Loved One*. While one supposes that the sometimes elaborate and expensive rituals of burial and the 'paying of last respects' are of no consequence to the dead, they may well have significance and value to the living. In some cases, however, particularly in the event of unexpected death, the funeral arrangements can prove distressing and the task altogether unfamiliar, for example, to a young widow. An understanding friend may thus be of practical help. Ensuring as far as possible that the funeral arrangements are appropriate can be of positive psychological value and a later source of comfort to the bereaved.

A number of organizations and agencies exist to help the bereaved. In Boston, Massachussets, for example, there is a Widows' Aide programme. Widows, who have successfully weathered their own losses, call upon newly bereaved women living in their area. They offer friendship, support, and advice. A comparable agency in Britain is called Cruse. This organization makes use of professionals such as social workers, clergymen, and doctors, who are willing to counsel bereaved people. Cruse also encourages self-help by setting up groups of widows who meet together for mutual support. The Samaritans are another organization, providing a telephone service for people in distress, to whom the bereaved may turn for advice and befriending by non-professional volunteers.

The clergyman's customary role includes visiting the sick, the dying, and the bereaved. Some pastors set great store by the vigilant performance of this function. There is no doubt that ministers of religion have the opportunity of being important 'resource-persons' and potent interveners in many family crises. They may bring great comfort to those who turn to them in distress. Yet clergymen, like the rest of us, may be anxious and defenceful when confronted with suffering and death. It is evident that formal religion plays a much smaller part in most people's lives than formerly and the clergyman may not be a familiar and knowledgeable friend of the family. If he resorts to what may appear, to his hearers at least, as high-sounding but empty jargon in an attempt at easy comfort, he will be ineffectual in their time of need. The clergyman's customary visit immediately after bereavement and his conducting of the funeral service brings him into contact with family members when they are probably still shocked and bemused. Not until sometime later will they be able to face their loss and begin the work of grieving. Unfortunately it is quite common for the initial support of relatives and friends to be withdrawn by this time, leaving the family to its heartbreak and its feelings of isolation. It may thus be advantageous for the clergyman to call during the week following the funeral, and he may need to pay several visits over succeeding weeks. He should be prepared to listen to feelings of resentment against God, the Church, and mankind generally. His acceptance of the expression of such bitter emotions and his refusal to give easy answers may help to reconcile the family to their loss. Even sincere and committed Christians may suffer a crisis of faith at the unforeseen loss of a loved one.

While the clergyman remains the person many people turn to in times of trouble and is by tradition the one who comforts those that mourn, people in Britain seek such help more and more from their family doctor. Sadly, they are more likely to get a prescription for tablets than a sympathetic hearing. Of course, sedatives, tranquillizers, and antidepressants have their important uses. In bereavement reactions, if utilized sparingly and insightfully, they may serve to reduce agitation and panic and control insomnia. They should not be used — but often are — as an alternative to helping the individual experience his grief. This task is inescapable if the bereaved person is to re-establish his normal equilibrium and to postpone it is dangerous.

Even in these days of group practice and deputizing services, many general practitioners get to know many of their patients intimately. If a family doctor has attended the dead person during his last illness, he has already got to know the family's strengths and weaknesses. He is well-placed to help them prepare for the crisis and is there to support them when it supervenes. The medical practitioner can also readily recruit the services of others — district nurse, health visitor, social worker, or psychiatrist.

The process of grieving does not terminate in a clear end-point. Islands of mourning may persist long after the acute phase is past. But it is common for people to recognize a critical event or turning-point. For example, a widow may finally accept an invitation to go out for the evening with a male escort; she may take up part-time employment; or she may go off on holiday and find that things fall into perspective. The realization dawns that life still offers fulfilment and pleasure. No longer imprisoned by grief, she is free to experience new relationships and can welcome change.

Atypical grief reaction

A morbid grief reaction tends to occur under certain circumstances. They may be listed as follows: (1) when the loss is overwhelming; (2) when anger and guilt are so intense that the loss is not clearly perceived or accepted; and

(3) when the necessary expression of sorrow is inhibited by personal or cultural factors. Those bereaved persons who become psychiatric casualties often show grief reactions that are either delayed or prolonged. As in any crisis, the outcome is determined by the interaction of the individual's personality and present stress, his past history, and the support available to him from family and community.

Two examples of bereavement reaction follow. They illustrate some of these features:

Case 1. Mrs. Thompson was a 32-year old schoolteacher who had given up her career to marry a farmer. They lived on a small, rather isolated croft. There were two young sons, the elder the apple of his mother's eye. Following a bout of influenza which left her tired and out-of-sorts, Mrs. Thompson agreed that her two sons should go off to live with their grandmother for a while to make things easier for her. A few days later, Ian, her favourite boy, was killed outside the school gates when he ran in front of a car. Mrs. Thompson shed a few tears at the boy's funeral and that was all. Her husband was a slow-moving, laconic countryman accustomed to keeping his feelings to himself. Fond as they were of each other, they seemed unable to express their distress in one another's presence. Mrs. Thompson slept badly, lost appetite and weight, and became frightened to leave the house. Her family doctor visited regularly and she confessed a great sense of blame for her son's death. Yet she had warned him often about crossing the road. If only she had not agreed to his going away to grandmother's, she complained. And angrily, why was it Ian who was killed? She became upset and resentful, quarrelled with her husband, and ignored the other child. The doctor prescribed pills which she did not take.

Nine months after her son's death she remained depressed, phobic, and housebound. Referred to the psychiatric clinic, she was seen regularly for out-patient psychotherapy. She talked a great deal about her son, his great promise at school, her blame for being ill and so sending him away, her guilt at not loving her other son the way she loved Ian, the emptiness of life, how neglectful she was of her husband, why was God punishing her in this way . . . . and so on. Over a period of several months she gradually improved. She began to take an interest again in her home, went shopping, and finally applied for a part-time teaching appointment. However, when seen later at follow-up, she was still so affected that she regularly took a long roundabout route when driving to town in order to avoid the graveyard where Ian was buried.

Case 2. Some 6 months after her husband's death, Mrs. Duncan, aged 50, was admitted to the psychiatric unit. She was an excessively polite, meticulous woman who was significantly depressed but tried to hide it behind false smiles and small talk. However, she complained at length about pains in her chest, that her sleep was disturbed, that she trembled a lot, and that people were conspiring against her. Her late husband, a University lecturer, had been devoted to books, bridge, and collecting antique furniture. He had suffered several heart attacks in the 5 years before his death. This had not prevented his amorous attachment to two other women.

Mrs. Duncan's earlier history was notable in that her own father had died when she was in her early teens. It was known also that she had experienced a period of depression after the birth of the first of her three children.

For 3 months before her admission Mrs. Duncan's general practitioner had been prescribing antidepressants and tranquillizers. The patient had taken these so zealously as to develop Parkinsonian tremor and rigidity. When the dosage was curtailed these side-effects vanished together with some of her suspicious attitude. In group psychotherapy (which initially she resented) she was encouraged to talk about her feelings, not hide them. This she managed to do, revealing a great store of anger and resentment against her husband. She felt she had been depressed for several months before his death, indeed since she discovered he was having an affair with one of his University colleagues. But when he died and she realized that she had been left with a large house full of old furniture and very little money, she became very upset. She resented his failure to make proper financial provision for her despite his knowledge over a period of years that he was in poor health. He had always been preoccupied with his own needs and his own social life and left her alone with the children much of the time. As a young woman she had given up her outside interests to care for a demanding husband, a growing family, and a large house. Then after his death she was left badly off and alone to be pestered by dealers who, she felt, were bent on cheating her over the sale of her husband's furniture.

In the group she confessed that perhaps she had never quite grown up. She had married her husband because he reminded her in some ways of her father and now she began to realize that a child-parent relationship in marriage could not have been very satisfactory for her husband either. This might go some way to explaining his need for other women. Discussion of these and other feelings helped Mrs. Duncan to emerge from her depression. She was able to accept her husband's death and to make sensible plans for the future.

These two case-histories serve to illustrate some features of atypical grief reaction. In both cases the dead person filled a central role. Mrs. Duncan had for many years before her husband's death entertained ambivalent feelings towards him; she depended on him and was angry at his neglect. In Mrs. Thompson's case there was long-standing, if well concealed, resentment that she had given up her chosen career to live on an isolated farm, distant from most cultural activities, and with a husband of limited education. Again, in both households, although support and sympathy were available, there was also the expectation of self-reliance and self-control. Neither woman was able to express her true feelings adequately except to the psychiatrist who was eventually involved.

Abnormal grief reactions fall into two main categories — (1) Delayed or Suppressed Reactions and (2) Chronic Reactions. Experience has demonstrated that, in both categories, one of the most important factors producing pathological responses is the absence of personal help. There is much evidence to suggest that the availability of a helper who has sympathy, knowledge, and time, may be critical in assisting the open expression of emotion and the acceptance of loss. The preventive function of crisis intervention is here clearly evident. As far as treatment of established abnormal reactions is concerned, one can only follow the basic principles already indicated. These are largely concerned with facilitating and making safe the outward expression of intense and sometimes complex emotions; thereafter realistic acceptance of loss is encouraged. If depressive symptoms are marked, suicidal intentions expressed, or more bizarre behaviour arises, referral to the psychiatrist and admission to in-patient care may be necessary. It should be emphasized, however, that no matter what specialized care is needed, bereavement is generally a family crisis and is best dealt with in the family. The professional roles of family doctor and clergyman should include effective support of family members and exploitation, where necessary, of other community resources. Doctor and clergyman might also be expected to give a lead in the establishment of effective services for the bereaved in their own locality.

CHAPTER 8

CRISIS AT LARGE : THE ADOLESCENT

THE crisis which brings a client to a helping agency is seldom the first of its kind. More often than not there is a past history of social difficulty, ineffectually resolved, which has paved the way for further disturbances. The individual or the family are ill-prepared to meet new stress and another crisis results. The following case illustrates such a sequence. It also demonstrates how difficult it may be to give effective help to a young person in trouble even when many resources are to hand and good intentions clearly evident.

Pamela, the young woman who is the central figure in this account, was referred to a psychiatric clinic by her general practitioner. In the short note which accompanied her he asked that she be assessed for termination of pregnancy. Pamela was then 14 years old. She presented as a physically attractive, if rather plump and sullen, young woman who looked older than her years. She was uncommunicative, hostile, and soon in tears. Her mother was seen — a well-dressed, rather tense woman, who announced that she herself had been a patient at the psychiatric clinic 2 years before. She was ready to embark on a long account of her life's troubles and seemed remarkably unconcerned about her daugher's predicament.

It quickly became apparent that there was, in fact, a long history of disturbance in this family with a complex field of forces acting and interacting on the three main protagonists — Pamela, her father, and her mother. During this first interview, from mother's account and by listening to Pam's angry exchanges, the psychiatrist gained the following information.

For most of her young life Pam had felt much closer to her father than her mother. They had enjoyed a warm relationship and spent much time together when she was a child. Mother often seemed to be in bed or ill with her 'nerves'. When Pam was 10 years old, mother had left home taking her two younger daughters with her. Father and Pam were left alone to look after themselves and the household. This was quite a happy time for Pam. But then her father introduced 'another woman' who came to live in the house, did the shopping and cooking, and took up her father's attention. Pam began to miss her mother and viewed the new arrival with a mixture of resentment and jealousy. After some months, this woman left the home and her mother and sisters returned. But the atmosphere was unhappy and disturbed by frequent rows between the parents. Moreover, Pam became aware that mother and father were often under the influence of alcohol and drugs and that father was pursuing a succession of lady-friends.

At this time Pam was doing well at school and was considered to be a girl of high intelligence. But she began to react to the disturbances at home by playing truant and running off to the home of distant relatives whom she called aunt and uncle. She also started to keep company with older boys at school and in the neighbourhood and, when father discovered this, he became angry. He laid down strict but inconsistent rules about where she might go, with whom, and by what time she must be home. In defiance, she not only missed school for several days but also went off with a gang of youths to another town. She was returned by the police and one officer suggested she should be medically checked for pregnancy and venereal disease. Her father accepted this suggestion with alacrity. Tests proved negative, but on each subsequent occasion that she left home he took her off 'for V.D. tests'. The relationship between Pam and her father deteriorated steadily thereafter. She described him to the psychiatrist as 'a beast'.

For several months before her referral to the clinic she had been keeping company with Brian who was 3 years her senior. He was disapproved of by her family because he was of lower social status and aggressive in his attitude and behaviour. However, it appeared likely that it was Brian's brother John, 10 years older than Pam and married, who had fathered her child. She said angrily that she wanted to be 'rid of it' and wished to leave school and find a job.

The psychiatrist also discovered that Miss Jolly of the City Social Work Department had been seeing Pam fairly regularly for some months. She had been involved with her following a visit to the Department by mother in a distraught state over Pam's general misbehaviour. The psychiatrist arranged for termination of the pregnancy. He got in touch with Miss Jolly, who agreed to intensify her contact with the girl and the family, and they further arranged to keep in regular communication about the case. Because of Pam's lack of co-operation with him, the psychiatrist felt that Miss Jolly's established relationship would prove more helpful. But he agreed to see the girl again should it appear necessary.

In fact, the psychiatrist heard no more until 8 months later. One of his junior colleagues was asked to see Pam at the casualty department of the gen-

eral hospital. She had been taken there with a self-inflicted injury, having cut
her wrists with a piece of broken glass. She was rude to the nurses and doctors
in the casualty department and refused to give any information about herself.
The young duty psychiatrist, who was female, was able to gain Pam's confidence. She learned that the termination of pregnancy had been performed
successfully. Pam had then returned to school, but not to the same one. Her
headmaster felt she was 'a bad influence' and 'out of control'. She was therefore transferred to another school serving a rather tough neighbourhood with
a less academically-inclined population. Miss Jolly had left the area to get
married. Before she went, she had quarrelled with Pam's father who said he
would not let her back into the house. Things at home were just as bad. Her
parents, on the family doctor's advice, had visited a marriage-guidance counsellor but failed to keep the further appointments offered. Pam said her parents were both regularly drunk and they also tippled on barbiturates and
amphetamines as well as 'tripping on acid' occasionally. In fact, her mother
had preceded her to the casualty department on two occasions recently because of self-poisoning. Mother had again been referred to the psychiatric
clinic and father was also asked to attend but refused to go. Pam said she saw
him quite often touring the streets in his car looking for a girl to pick-up.

The wrist injuries were minor. They were inflicted impulsively by Pam on
her way home in a sudden mood of despair, although she could not describe
exactly why. Pam was allowed to go back home that night from the casualty
department. The duty psychiatrist reported these developments to her senior
(the psychiatrist originally involved with Pam) next day at the clinic. What
should be done now? After discussion, it was agreed that Mrs. Denny, a social
worker attached to the clinic and experienced in mental health, should try to
pick up from Miss Jolly and see Pam regularly. Mrs. Denny got in touch with
Pam who agreed to come to see her at the clinic regularly and this contact was
more or less maintained over the subsequent year. During this time several
crises occurred.

At their first interview, after some preliminary conversation of a general
nature, Mrs. Denny asked Pam to talk about the circumstances in which she
had cut her wrists. It transpired that Pam had been feeling unusually pleased
with life just before this event. She was doing well at her new school and was
studying for examinations. She also had a boy friend, Charlie, with whom she
had been keeping company for 3 months. She had become fond of him and
had started to dress in a more feminine and attractive way in order to please
him, for example, abandoning her usual jeans for a dress. Charlie was the

school Casanova and she was flattered that she was his chosen girl-friend. They had sexual intercourse frequently and Charlie had gone with her to her general practitioner to ask that a contraceptive pill be prescribed for her. Their relationship seemed to be stable and serious. Then suddenly she heard one day at school that he was going out with another girl and had said he had finished with Pam. Her exams began next day. She was keen to do well and, although upset by the news of her boy friend's behaviour, she went home that evening to study. She found the house full of people, all drinking and making a lot of noise. Her father was so drunk that he had been put to bed. Her own room was occupied by the young children of her parents' drinking friends downstairs. She felt this was the last straw and began to shout and weep; but no one paid her much attention. She flung out of the house feeling angry, rejected and misunderstood. Later that evening she cut her wrists.

During their first few meetings together, Mrs. Denny encouraged Pam to express her feelings about Charlie and her parents. She listened to Pam's ambitions, how she wanted to proceed from school to University, and she indicated her interest, approval, and general support. Pam said there were a number of boys at school interested in her and who wanted to date her, but she found them boring. She met Charlie sometimes and would like to have him back. Mrs. Denny wondered out loud why Pam should avoid relationships with boys who were fond of her and whom she might trust, and preferred Charlie who had already shown himself unfaithful and who would almost certainly hurt her again if she let him.

A working therapeutic relationship was established between Pam and Mrs. Denny. They met regularly at the clinic and things seemed to be going fairly well. Pam's parents were still drinking excessively and having rows. Pam herself was going out with a number of different young men and allowed herself on one occasion to be seduced by the instructor at the riding-stables she attended. She told this to Mrs. Denny with a mixture of shame and satisfaction, describing the instructor as 'a dirty old man'. One day she spoke of the termination of her pregnancy, admitting that usually she tried to forget the whole matter 'otherwise I'd feel like a murderer'. At the end of school term she had done well and won several prizes.

During school vacation she took a temporary job at a cafe. This gave her money of her own and perhaps a sense of greater independence. Her parents at this point of time were enjoying an armistice and both were trying to exert more consistent control over her activities. This she resented and confessed to Mrs. Denny that in some ways she preferred her parents to be fighting.

One weekend, after Pam had stayed out all night and then confessed her sexual relationships with several young men, father became enraged and mother announced that she was nothing but a whore. The resultant row decided Pam to leave home and school, go south, and find employment. She hitched a lift to London, but felt unhappy and lonely, and returned home after 3 weeks thin and unkempt. Mrs. Denny then received a telephone call from Pam's headmaster. He had just learned from the girl herself of her difficulties at home and that she was attending a psychiatric clinic. He felt she had a lot of promise academically but was unhappy about her home circumstances and her general behaviour. Could she leave her parents without their consent and be looked after elsewhere? Mrs. Denny felt this was unlikely but telephoned the Reporter of the Children's Panel and also the City Social Work Department. The Reporter felt he held no authority or responsibility in the case since Pam was over 16 years of age. The Social Work Department said they could arrange accommodation for the girl away from home if her parents consented. Mrs. Denny visited the parents who expressed anger at the suggestion and refused to discuss it.

The next few months were disturbed for Pam and unsatisfactory for those trying to help her. She did not attend school and went to work in a restaurant. She did not keep her appointments with Mrs. Denny but occasionally turned up unexpectedly and asked to be seen. She announced, none too convincingly, that she was happy at work and looking for a flat of her own. She visited the school and confided to her year-master that she was fed-up with her job and would like to come back to classes. Things were going badly for her at home and after a further quarrel with her parents she went off to live with a boy friend. In these circumstances the headmaster felt it unwise to re-admit her to school. Mrs. Denny and the clinic psychiatrist discussed the situation but, since Pam was over 16, it was not possible to take her 'into care' against her own and her parents' wishes. Mrs. Denny was encouraged to continue her availability to Pam in the hope of influencing her towards more sensible behaviour. In fact Pam herself did not appear for several months, but one day her father came to the clinic and was interviewed by Mrs. Denny and by the psychiatrist who had seen Pam originally. Father had been drinking. He was also upset and tearful, saying he was to blame for Pam, but his wife more so. 'She's nothing short of an alcoholic' he shouted angrily, announcing his intention of leaving her. He ended the session by abusing psychiatry and social work generally, and the clinic psychiatrist and Mrs. Denny in particular, leaving the building with the assurance he would never darken its doors again. In fact he died a year later, following self-poisoning by drugs and alcohol.

A few weeks after her seventeenth birthday Pam was seen again at the clinic. She was referred by the Court for a psychiatric assessment following the theft of £50 and a bottle of whisky from the home of her 'uncle', the relative she had run to as a girl when in trouble at home. In the company of another young woman, she had broken into the house one evening when her relatives were out. She knew her 'uncle' kept a sum of ready money at home and where to look for it. She admitted the offence readily, but said they were both drunk at the time and she really remembered little about it.

From this interview, the psychiatrist learned that since her last visit to the clinic Pam had been in lots of trouble. The boy friend she lived with after leaving home became fed-up with her and had emigrated to Australia. Soon after, she discovered she was pregnant again. 'I was afraid and disgusted at first,' she said, 'but I began to think I'd like to have something of my own. If nobody cares for me at least I can care for someone, that's what I thought.' Without a home or money she decided to go to her parents. But father got angry when he heard she was pregnant and refused to accept her back. Thereafter she got mixed up in the local drug scene, 'slept around', and had a miscarriage. For a while she was depressed and thought of committing suicide. However, she found a friend in the person of another girl 'drop-out' with whom, in search of money to buy drink or drugs, she had broken into her 'uncle's' house.

She appeared for the interview with the psychiatrist well-dressed and self-assured. She answered questions frankly and talked about herself in a straightforward way, appearing co-operative and realistic. It was as though the police charge and her Court appearance had brought her to a realization of her condition and her unhappy prospects if she continued along the road she had started upon.

She had obtained a part-time job and was living with a respectable girl friend. She was planning to get better employment and attend night school. At one point in the interview she talked wistfully of her previous ambitions to go to University and be a biologist. But her attitude of self-sufficiency was soon resumed. She made plain that she wanted no help from the psychiatric clinic and she thought it unreasonable that there should be any question of her 'sanity'. She was grown-up now and intended to go her own way and lead her own life.

The psychiatrist was in some doubt as to what to recommend to the Court. Although known to the police, Pam was a first offender. Committal to residential care had to be considered in view of her past history and disturbed home background; but it seemed to have more disadvantages than benefits. Even allowing for the fact that she might be putting on a front, he felt that she had come to a realistic appraisal of her situation. Perhaps with suitable support she could find her way back to self-respect and towards a fulfilling life. He consulted Mrs. Denny and they both agreed he should recommend that the Court make a probation order. Since Pam was hostile to any suggestion of formal psychiatric treatment, the order should not be made under the Mental Health Act; but a probation officer would see her regularly, might gain her co-operation and trust, and be able to supervise her behaviour.

The psychiatrist looked thoughtfully at Mrs. Denny and asked what they might have done differently. Could a more thorough early appraisal or more vigorous intervention have prevented some of the crises and led to a more constructive outcome? What might have been done which was not done? With the advantage of hindsight, the following observations and criticisms may be offered.

1. A count reveals fifteen different 'helping-agents' involved with Pam — mainly doctors, social workers, schoolteachers, and police. Some attempts were made at co-operation, for example between the senior psychiatrist at the clinic and the social workers involved. But attempts at co-operation between other agencies were tentative. Indeed, this is the main criticism to be offered: that most of the efforts devoted to helping Pam were aimed at her as an individual and were given by individuals.

2. The general practitioner remains a distant figure throughout the account, although he must have been involved frequently with various members of the family. The initial referral letter, which took Pam to the psychiatrist for an opinion on termination of pregnancy, was laconic and unhelpful and made no attempt to describe the current state of affairs at home. The G.P. may have felt that mother's previous contact with the psychiatric clinic meant that information was already available. However, his contacts with Pam through her 'V.D. tests' and her request for contraception, his awareness of the faulty marriage, and his first-hand knowledge of the total family situation were not put to use. Family doctors tend to be over-worked, their time is at a premium, and many of them feel at a disadvantage when dealing with complaints that are other than physical. On the other hand, those who take an active interest in the psychological ills of their patients are powerful allies in dealing with family crises. In Pam's case, no energetic attempt was made to involve the family doctor in the treatment strategy.

3. The various schoolteachers involved with Pam, including one or two with whom she evidently enjoyed a comfortable relationship, seemed to work in isolation with her problems as they presented at school. The advent in Britain of the guidance-teacher or year-master has given sanction to the school's function as intervener in a pupil's personal problems as well as his educational or vocational difficulties. Since it has been estimated[26] that the average pupil spends 11,000 hours at school, the potential for what might be termed 'therapeutic encounter' seems enormous. Until recently, however, teachers have been preoccupied with matters of discipline and the teaching of school subjects. Any other influence of teacher upon pupil has been largely intuitive and haphazard. The guidance-teacher is often unsure of his role and of his commitment to counselling which may involve not only the pupil but perhaps also the family. The anxiety is easily understandable since most guidance-teachers have received meagre training for their new function. Moreover, as Pam's case illustrates, it is easy for the pupil to slip between the meshes of the various systems. Communication and collaboration between school and other agencies is often poor and sometimes even non-existent. Instead of close working relationships between school and Child Guidance Clinic, Educational Psychology Service, Youth Employment Officer, Local Authority Social Work Service, and Probation Officer, and intelligent use of a Parent-Teacher's Association, there may be indifference to and ignorance of one another's needs and resources.

In Pam's case there seems to have been no contact at all between Miss Jolly, Local Authority Social Worker, and the school. And the contact between Mrs. Denny, the clinic social worker, and Pam's headmaster was confined to one or two telephone conversations. The question must arise as to whether a more integrated approach to the disturbances and crises evident at school, might have prevented at least some of Pam's later difficulties.

4. The police were formally involved when Pam engaged in housebreaking and theft. However, she had been apprehended by them on several previous occasions when she ran away from home. Her first pregnancy, when she was 14, followed her association with an older man; he thus committed an offence, but these circumstances were not made known to the police at that time. In fact the police were well acquainted with the family. Father had committed a number of driving offences, and the parents' misuse of drugs and alcohol had caused disturbances in the house and complaints by neighbours.

Police vary widely in their approach to disturbed adolescents. Some are punitive and others sympathetic. Few receive much in the way of information or instruction and close working relationships with psychiatric agencies are rare. The Social Work Acts in Britain have altered their formal procedure with young offenders and may render them less sure of their role. In Pam's case the police played their part in isolation and received no request for collaboration.

5. Local authority social work departments in Britain have expanded enormously since the implementation of the Social Work Acts. But, even so, the load of service they have been asked to carry has been overwhelming. Young social workers like Miss Jolly, with·little in the way of relevant experience and without sufficient supervision, have been asked to shoulder responsibilities beyond their capabilities. The situation is changing as staff and training facilities increase.

Miss Jolly was warmly disposed towards Pam but she did not really understand what was happening to the girl and felt inadequate to deal with the home situation. She therefore kept at a distance from Pam's parents until she finally had a row with father just before leaving the area. She also maintained a safe relationship with Pam and did not challenge her unsuitable views and self-destructive behaviour. Because of this lack of involvement, she felt no need to keep in touch with the psychiatrist, let him know when she left, or even make firm arrangements to transfer Pam's case to a colleague. Once more the criticism of professional isolation can be made.

6. The clinic psychiatrist and social worker sought to co-operate closely in Pam's case. Mrs. Denny's relationship with Pam was intelligently nurtured and utilized to encourage the patient to recognize her problems, understand them, and find better ways of dealing with them. It was quickly evident to both workers that much of Pam's behaviour could be interpreted in terms of faulty family relationships. For example, her mother's lack of warmth towards her from an early age, together with several periods of separation, severely damaged their relationship. Pam turned to her father and, for a time, found the warmth and closeness she sought. Mother became a rival. Later, Pam seemed to be playing-out for both parents some of their sexual fantasies. As she grew into a physically attractive young woman, she and her parents became enmeshed in their common problems of sexuality, dependency, and authority. Mother, father, and daughter were all behaving in a disturbed fashion by this time, each appearing to activate the other.

Despite their awareness of this, the psychiatrist and social worker erred in two ways, Firstly, they failed to give a clear lead in crossing professional boundaries and recruiting help, for example from family doctor and school staff. Secondly, they continued to deal with Pam as an individual in trouble and did not involve her parents in therapy. While accepting the real difficulties of intervention in this 'sick' family, it seems an error of judgment to neglect the opportunities provided by conjoint family therapy. Such an approach would have acknowledged that the disturbance lay not within one individual but rather within the family's pattern of relationships. Moreover, by opening channels of communication through the family's forbidden areas, it might have given the members the opportunity and the freedom to change. Pam and her family together might then have found a pathway through crisis to an acceptable compromise.

CHAPTER 9

CRISIS IN THE SUPERMARKET

SHOPLIFTING is a common offence and the growth of self-service stores has undoubtedly provided great opportunities for undetected pilfering. It appears that some citizens look upon petty theft of this kind as being unlawful merely in a technical sense — rather as motorists ignore speed limits. Gibbens[27] investigating the mental health aspects of shoplifting, noted how many cases dealt with in the London West-End courts concerned young women who were well brought up and normally honest. He found sex and age to be important variables which differentiate various kinds of shoplifters. For example, male shoplifters differ from female in that approximately half the men convicted steal books, the theft of which is almost unknown in women. In addition, half the men have previous convictions of all kinds and a third have spent time in prison. In contrast, 80 per cent of women shoplifters are first offenders and the reconviction rate is only 10 per cent. Of the group of female London shoplifters examined by Professor Gibbens and his associates in 1971, nearly one-third were foreign-born. Indeed this category comprised half the number of younger offenders. In British-born women the peak age for shoplifting is between 50 and 60 years. Many female shoplifters of this age — at least the ones who are apprehended and examined — appear to be suffering from depression.

Gibbens[27] describes the typical shoplifter of this kind as follows. 'She is a woman of fifty who a year before had a hysterectomy and has not felt well since. She has backaches, headaches, dizziness, insomnia, and a persistent sense of depression. She sometimes gets up in the night to turn off the gas or to see that the door is locked. She has no serious financial difficulties, but her husband and children take no notice of her and she feels that life in the future stretches out like a desert. She has been seeing her doctor regularly and receiving tranquillizers, but she has not been to him for three months because she feels she is wasting his time.'

Of course, not all female shoplifters fit this description. In some the theft is precipitated by obvious stress. In younger women this may be a recent miscarriage, a bereavement, or some other kind of personal loss. Sometimes the episode of shoplifting seems to be a way of punishing husband or family by bringing shame to them by association and, at the same time, gaining their attention and perhaps their concern. Occasionally a woman of good character who is convicted of shoplifting repeats the offence. This may be due to a recurrence of stress or depression, or even because she feels the first conviction ruined her reputation for good. One middle-aged lady of the writer's acquaintance, who felt neglected by her husband, turned for solace to alcohol; but she marked the anniversary of her son's death, year after year, by shoplifting. Another, an elderly shoplifter convicted on three separate occasions despite lengthy psychiatric treatment, finally secured her husband's close attention and curtailed his individual recreational activities because he found it necessary to accompany her wherever she went in order to prevent further repetition of the offence. The following case-history illustrates such features, while focussing on what constituted a crisis in one woman's life.

Mrs. Earl, a large, plump, motherly-looking woman of 60, was a familiar figure in her home town, a county township that was small enough for most people to know most others by sight. Mrs. Earl, however, was one of those who kept herself to herself. She was respected as a hard-working widow who had been left, aged 30, by the death of her husband, to bring up two young daughters. Her husband was killed while serving in the forces and she had a War pension which she supplemented by working as a domestic in the local cottage hospital. At the time of the crisis to be described, she had been retired from her employment a month or two. Her daughters were grown up, married, and occupied with their own affairs. She found time hanging heavy on her hands. In the past she had always kept busy and was inclined to be fussy and houseproud. Now she started to neglect the house and did not even cook proper meals for herself. She missed the company of her fellow-workers, was worried about the rising cost of living, and she felt lonely – particularly in the evenings. She had visited her family doctor who tried to reassure her, told her to go out more, and prescribed a mild sleeping-pill. He was taken aback, a week or two later, to receive a telephone call from the local sergeant of police who announced that Mrs. Earl had been charged with shoplifting from the town's supermarket. Moreover, the sergeant made plain to Dr. Dixon that there was cause for anxiety over Mrs. Earl's state of mind and he suggested a call on the patient as a matter of urgency.

This the doctor did and found Mrs. Earl sitting at home agitated, tearful, and distressed. She told her story which amounted in essence to the fact that she had put some groceries into her shopping-bag, rather than the supermarket basket she was also carrying, and had failed to pay for them. Her action was noted by one of the store assistants who called the manager. Mrs. Earl became very upset, said she did not remember putting the articles in her own bag, had no intention of stealing them, and she offered to pay for the goods. The manager would not heed her pleas and protestations and called the police. The police sergeant took statements from those concerned and, recognizing Mrs. Earl's agitation and distress, later escorted her home. Realizing she was alone in the house, he decided to call Dr. Dixon. He wondered if she might even be suicidal.

Dr. Dixon had known Mrs. Earl and her family for many years. He listened to her account and encouraged her to express her feelings. He knew she had not been feeling well for some time and got her to talk about this too. Mrs. Earl told how life had seemed to lose its interest for her of late. Particularly since leaving her employment in the hospital she felt lost and lonely. She had no interest in housework or cooking, she was sleeping poorly, and lacked energy. She paid regular visits to her married daughters, but there was no warmth of contact and she did not try to explain to them how she was feeling. 'I couldn't burden them with my troubles, doctor. They've got plenty of their own.' In fact she never had been able to share her feelings with anyone and certainly not with her daughters. She became upset at the very thought of them, saying, 'What are they going to think of me? What will they say when they learn their mother is a thief?' Sobbing she cried out that she would be better dead. Dr. Dixon tried to reassure and comfort her and obtained her consent to his calling one of her daughters. He explained what had happened and arranged for Mrs. Earl to go to her daughter's home for at least that night.

Unfortunately, even in the throes of her distress, Mrs. Earl was unable to confide in her daughters. She went to her bedroom and cried there quietly, saying very little to either daughter when they tried to engage her in talk. It later was made plain that the relationship between mother and daughters had never been close. Mrs. Earl had never talked to them about their dead father. When they were children she brushed their questions aside and did not share with them her own worry and feelings of loss. The two girls grew up with a view of their mother as a competent, self-sufficient, and rather hard woman. They respected her and were dutiful; but they felt at a distance from her and out-of-touch with her deeper concerns. For her part, Mrs. Earl felt she had done her best to protect her young daughters from painful emotions and she prided herself on having hidden her tears and fears from them. When these matters were finally exposed in the family, Mrs. Earl was astonished to hear that her behaviour had led her daughters to view her as uncaring and unapproachable. In view of all this, it is not surprising that at the moment of crisis Mrs. Earl found herself unable to share her burden or ventilate her feelings in an easy or open fashion. For their part, her daughters were puzzled and alarmed. Recognizing a change in their mother, and that she was vulnerable after all, they still found it difficult to respond in a satisfactory way.

Dr. Dixon was a thoughtful and sensitive family doctor who, more often than not, found time to talk to his patients and recognized the limitations of medication in the treatment of psychological ills. He arranged for Mrs. Earl to come to his surgery and he examined her physically. He found her overweight and her blood-pressure was higher than it should have been. Otherwise, she appeared to be in fairly good physical health. Her recent history was strongly suggestive of a depressive illness and her shoplifting, which was quite out of character, seemed to indicate emotional disorder of this kind. He decided to prescribe an anti-depressant; but he also arranged to meet Mrs. Earl and her two daughters together. In addition he brought into the situation, after discussing it fully with her, Miss Norton, the social worker who liaised with his practice. The five of them sat down together one afternoon and it was on this occasion that the feelings of both daughters for their mother came to light. Perhaps as a result of this confrontation, Mrs. Earl revealed her own feelings more openly than ever before, even to the extent of confessing her loneliness and despair after her husband's death, and the burden she experienced of bringing up two young children alone. The immediate result of the out-pouring of emotion was to bring Mrs. Earl and her daughters into closer relationship and greater understanding of one another.

Dr. Dixon felt an important barrier had been jumped. The new situation in Mrs. Earl's family, he was confident, would preclude any suicidal behaviour on her part and he hoped she could now re-establish her emotional well-being and social competence. He asked Miss Norton to arrange to visit Mrs. Earl further and he called to see the police sergeant. The sergeant was sympathetic when he heard the story and, after consultation and discussion with the chief constable, it was arranged that the charge of shoplifting against Mrs. Earl would be abandoned. Mrs. Earl was very pleased and relieved to hear this news. Her depression and agitation improved markedly and, after a few days, she insisted on returning to her own home. There Miss Norton continued to visit her.

In fact it took around 9 months for Mrs. Earl to return to her normal state. Dr. Dixon continued to prescribe an anti-depressant pill for her and this reduced her symptoms. Miss Norton visited her regularly, helped her to budget her expenditure against her income, listened to her expressions of inadequacy and guilt, and supported her hopefully through recurrent moods of sadness and gloom. She suggested further joint meetings of the family, that is mother, daughters, and herself, but there was always some difficulty in finding a suitable time. Miss Norton felt that all three were rather embarrassed at the revelations of their first meeting and were anxious lest they said anything further which might hurt. The two daughters nevertheless visited their mother regularly, were concerned and supportive, and clearly there was an improvement in their relationships.

Dr. Dixon became anxious at Mrs. Earl's lack of progress. He telephoned a psychiatrist colleague and outlined the story to him. The psychiatrist arranged to see Mrs. Earl, also spoke to Miss Norton, and expressed the view that no other intervention seemed necessary. He reassured Dr. Dixon and Miss Norton that what they were doing appeared appropriate, but promised that, if progress did not become more obvious soon, he would arrange a course of E.C.T. (electro-convulsive therapy) for Mrs. Earl. In fact Mrs. Earl began to brighten up shortly after. She regained an interest in her appearance and the state of her household, and began to visit her grandchildren and look-up her own friends. One day she went with Miss Norton to shop in the supermarket. She felt embarrassed, particularly on coming face to face with the manager, but was quite elated afterwards that she had managed to go and shop there.

Comment

This crisis had a satisfactory and constructive outcome. However, it might have ended tragically in Mrs. Earl's suicide but for the vigilance and sensitivity of the sergeant of police and the care given to her by others. The family doctor found time to listen to her and encouraged the expression of feelings — something Mrs. Earl had never found easy. He arranged for family support and contrived at least the beginnings of fuller and freer communication between mother and daughters. With the help of the community-based social worker, he continued to take responsibility for treating Mrs. Earl but, recognizing his own anxiety at the lack of dramatic improvement, did not hesitate to get more expert advice and reassurance from the psychiatrist. Miss Norton was able to befriend Mrs. Earl, give her practical help with running her home, and she aided her in recognizing, accepting, and expressing feelings she had suppressed for years. There seems no doubt that Mrs. Earl's shoplifting was a consequence of, and probably an expression of, a moderately severe depression. It may be interpreted as a cry for help or as a symbolic 'taking' of emotional supplies of which she was so sorely in need. One might further speculate that this crisis had its roots in the loss of her husband 30 years before, a crisis which was not adequately resolved at that time because she denied rather than expressed her grief. Misguidedly, she refused to allow her young daughters to share any of their or her feelings at their mutual loss. Her independent stance and apparent lack of emotion antagonized the two girls and the family failed to achieve cohesion or warmth. The shoplifting crisis exploded the situation and led to a degree of new discovery of one another. This brought comfort and pleasure to the extended family in the years which followed.

CHAPTER 10

CRISIS AT SCHOOL

TOMMY was a curly-haired attractive-looking boy of 9 who provided his school-teacher, Mrs. Taylor, with a considerable problem. She herself was young, inexperienced, and by nature rather anxious. Tommy ensured that she had always something to be anxious about. He was stubborn and aggressive, sometimes played the role of the class 'clown', could be affable and co-operative in his sunny moments, but generally was occupied in some form of misbehaviour. Occasionally he engaged in temper-tantrums. At such times he would lie on the floor kicking and screaming. Nevertheless he revealed evidence of a good intelligence and creative ability in the stories he wrote and the pictures he painted in class.

Mrs. Taylor gave him special consideration and attention and, at times, Tommy responded appreciatively. More often he was rude, argued with her, frolicked round the classroom, and jostled and upset the other pupils. In order to deal with episodes of particularly disturbing behaviour she had to call the headmaster. On such occasions Tommy might begin by interfering with his classmates at their work. When asked to desist he would in fact increase his irritating conduct. He would flick ink or fling plasticine at them, pull their hair, trip them up, and race round the room. Any attempt to restrain him at this stage met with abuse, swearing, and angry flailing of fists and feet. Sometimes he ran from the classroom, but noticeably he never ran home. When the headmaster removed Tommy bodily from the class in such circumstances, it was remarkable how his shouting and bluster died as soon as he quit the room. The head teacher and Mrs. Taylor discussed together what was to be done about Tommy. The headmaster recognized Mrs. Taylor's anxiety and inexperience, but also that she was committed to understanding and handling Tommy more effectively. They decided to ask Tommy's parents to call at the school and talk over the situation.

The four of them met in the headmaster's office. Mr. Phillips, Tommy's father, was a slim, tense-looking man in his early thirties. His wife, who 'took over' the interview, was a good-looking but rather sullen-featured blonde in her late twenties. The headmaster began by explaining the staff's anxieties and difficulties with Tommy, but he was soon interrupted by Mrs. Phillips, who accused him of disliking her son and failing to understand his particular needs. The head teacher became aware of a wave of hostility directed towards him from Tommy's mother, but he could not understand why or how he should deal with it. Mr. Phillips tried to intervene in a conciliatory way, but was ignored by his wife. Mrs. Taylor was able to express some of her concern and her growing feelings of helplessness in the face of Tommy's behaviour. She also mentioned how Tommy at times showed exaggerated fears. For example, he was scared of swimming or of visiting the school nurse, and indeed on such occasions got into a state of panic. Mrs. Phillips became somewhat subdued at this point and said that she knew of Tommy's anxieties. 'He takes after me. I've been attending the psychiatrist myself for similar symptoms.' Little further emerged from this interview.

A few weeks later the headmaster asked the Phillips to come to see him again. Tommy's behaviour had shown no improvement. Indeed one day he had attacked the music teacher because he felt he was being mocked and laughed at. The head teacher suggested the need for more expert assessment and help for the boy and announced his intention of referring him to the Child Guidance Centre. Somewhat to his surprise, Mrs. Phillips accepted this recommendation without argument.

Tommy and his parents were seen at the Centre and the following information was gained. He was the eldest of three. When he was 4 years old his parents separated for about 18 months and during that period he had been ill and been for some weeks in the Children's Hospital. He was admitted for investigation because of 'turns' which, it was thought, might be epileptic in nature. In fact, no firm diagnosis was made, but the opinion was given that his 'turns' were probably emotional in origin.

During interview the parents seemed anxious and guarded, particularly at first. They answered questions briefly, and it was sometime before any information was offered spontaneously. However, it emerged that Mrs. Phillips was herself the product of a broken home, her father separating from his family when she was 3 years old. For several years she was in residential care and still had mixed feelings about this period, although now emotionally close to her mother whom she visited frequently. For some years she had suffered from 'nerves' and intermittently had attended a psychiatric clinic. She had suffered episodes of depression and, on more than one occasion, had swallowed an overdose of sleeping-pills. However, she felt she was now being helped by her present psychiatrist who had arranged to see her and her husband together in marital therapy. She did not really want to talk about that aspect of things any further. Mr. Phillips began to speak at this point. He told how they had been married 10 years. Their relationship had always been stormy, largely because of his wife's moods and her dependence on drugs. Also she drank too much at times and he was not pleased at some of the company she kept. He and his wife often had rows. They disagreed about the children and he felt his wife was too strict, demanding unrealistically high standards of behaviour from them. She got angry and slapped them for minor faults. Tommy, in particular, he felt was reacting to the disturbed atmosphere at home. By this time Mrs. Phillips was glaring at her husband and he said no more.

Psychological testing confirmed that Tommy was of good average intelligence. He was inconsistent in his performance, however. He also revealed profound anxieties of a phobic nature concerning illness, death, injury, drowning, doctors, and hospitals.

At their staff meeting, the Child Guidance team discussed what action should be taken with Tommy and his family. It was evident that Mrs. Taylor, his teacher, needed support to continue with Tommy and it would be appropriate for an educational psychologist to work with her and with the school situation. Besides this, more information about Tommy might be obtained and some help provided for him by play therapy. A regular session could be arranged at the Centre. It was further suggested that one of the Centre social workers might maintain contact with the parents and liaise with the psychiatrist who was treating them. In the event, the main focus of attention became the situation at school. Both parents felt they were getting the help they needed from the psychiatrist. They did not wish to see the social worker or return to the Child Guidance Centre. They had no objections to Tommy having play therapy, but it was their opinion that too much was being made of the whole issue.

When the educational psychologist visited Mrs. Taylor he found her most willing to talk about her anxieties. She was receptive to the idea of regular meetings with him. These occurred weekly for about 2 months with little perceptible change in the situation. Tommy's behaviour varied, but more often than not he was difficult and disturbing. One day the psychologist received a telephone call from the headmaster asking whether he could visit the school urgently. An emergency had blown up over Tommy, and Mrs. Taylor at that moment was in his office in tears. The psychologist was able to respond and went immediately to join Mrs. Taylor and the headteacher. By this time Mrs. Taylor had dried her tears, but she was obviously upset. She told how Tommy had been misbehaving all week. Indeed his lack of co-operation had never been so extreme. A number of complaints from other parents had arrived at the school questioning the apparent lack of discipline in the class and how their children had been molested by Tommy. The climax was reached that morning. The class were engaged in modelling with clay. Tommy would not settle to the task and started to interfere with other pupils' activities. At one point he picked up a lump of clay and threw it at one of his classmates; but it missed its target and broke the classroom window. This startled everyone including Tommy. He leapt round the room scattering books and chairs and some of the children started to scream. Mrs. Taylor, alarmed at what was happening, managed to grab him. He flailed with his fists and struck her hard on the nose. In pain and anger, Mrs. Taylor struck back. Then she became even more upset and fled the room in tears. She sought out the headmaster who quelled the uproar in class and then berated Tommy in a furious tone.

The psychologist listened to this account and expressed the view that enough was enough. He said he recognized how hard Mrs. Taylor and the head teacher had tried to win Tommy over and how little they had been rewarded. He could well understand how Mrs. Taylor had reacted to Tommy in the circumstances and had slapped him. Most others would have done the same. Indeed he wondered if a more direct expression of anger towards Tommy might not have helped at an earlier stage. He did not mean physical chastisement so much as a clear communication of feelings to Tommy and a firm setting of limits. But it was evident now that Tommy was unmanageable. He would make arrangements for his transfer from school. The headmaster agreed but, to their surprise, Mrs. Taylor did not. She expressed the feeling that the crisis had cleared the air and might give the opportunity of a new beginning. She recognized that she had been angry with Tommy for months and had been fearful of accepting such an emotion, far less of expressing it. She had felt her anger to be unworthy of her and that it would destroy her relationship with Tommy. She believed this had been, to some extent at least, a mistake and now that her anger had been openly vented, and the headmaster's also, it might put her on a better footing with Tommy. To give up now would leave her with a great sense of failure. Could she not have another attempt?

Some further discussion led to an agreement that Tommy's teacher should continue her relationship with him. Subsequent weeks and months demonstrated that this crisis did in fact mark a turning-point. Mrs. Taylor seemed to find a new confidence and freedom in her relationship with Tommy and was able to express approval or disapproval more easily. The boy himself also recognized that the tolerance of his teachers had limits and he had reached them.

Information of a guarded nature given by the psychiatrist indicated that there was continuing disturbance in the home. The parents were quarrelling, Mrs. Phillips was drinking heavily at times, and she was consorting with other men. Tommy was under considerable stress, therefore, and his behaviour at school sometimes showed it. He was able to express some of his fears and conflicts in play therapy at the Centre. At school there was an understanding of the position, although also some frustration that the unhappy home situation, which was so basic to Tommy's disturbance, was also so out of reach. This was discussed by the psychologist and Mrs. Taylor. They accepted that there was unlikely to be any active co-operation from the parents. Whatever the actual stresses at home, Tommy's behaviour at school would have to be treated within that setting and the limits of action acknowledged.

In fact Tommy's behaviour in class improved. There was a relapse when his mother and father separated. Thereafter he settled down to live with his father and appeared to benefit from this more stable and consistent relationship. Mrs. Taylor perceived that not all the upsets in her class derived from Tommy and that sometimes he had been made a scapegoat for other pupils. Mr. Phillips visited the school and was happy to consult Mrs. Taylor and the headmaster over his son's behaviour. Tommy responded appropriately; and when the time came for him to move from Mrs. Taylor's class he had achieved a considerable improvement.

Comment

The Western world abounds with impressive theories of education, but one often wonders where they are put into practice. In most countries schools grow larger, more complex, and impersonal. Enlightened teachers challenge the assumptions of educational tradition, schools change, and yet it seems that fundamentally everything remains much as it was. In *The Underachieving School* Holt[28] offers this comment: 'Almost every child, on the first day he sets foot in a school building, is smarter, more curious, less afraid of what he doesn't know, better at finding and figuring things out, more confident, resourceful, persistent, and independent, than he will ever again be in his schooling or, unless he is very unusual and lucky, for the rest of his life.' What an indictment − if there is any truth in this statement at all − of our educational system!

Morris[29] has emphasized how much territory is shared by educationists, psychologists, sociologists, and psychiatrists. 'However,' he complains, 'the area in question seems more frequently to be viewed as disputed territory rather than common ground.' Recently there have been signs of a more tolerant attitude, but a genuine and full sharing of aims and methods is seldom achieved. Teachers tend to scoff at 'mental health' as an educational aim, pointing out that it is not the pupil's role to be a patient, nor the teacher's to be a therapist. Such a statement illustrates an all-too-frequent but quite mistaken conception of what mental health is all about. It ignores the fact that a child's development cannot be divided into separate compartments. He receives his education, for good or ill, in his family and his community, as well as in his school. Faulty learning in one area can possibly be remedied in another. But not if they remain divided, remote from one another, and fail to interact. In an ideal society, these different facets would match and be all of a piece.

It is disputable how many children are presently rescued by their schooling from adverse influences in home or neighbourhood. It is also arguable how many more might be happier and more creative if schools paid greater heed to their role in mental health. The advent of guidance teachers may mark a new awareness of this responsibility and opportunity.

In the case of Tommy, the boy described in this chapter, stress at home was an obvious cause of his behavioural disturbance. His mother was herself severely disturbed, demonstrating neurotic symptoms, dependence on drugs and alcohol, and also considerable difficulties in her relationships with the opposite sex. Much of this seemed to stem, in its turn, from her disrupted early life and her seeming abandonment by father and mother. To some extent history was repeating itself with Tommy. He was close to being a casualty and that he did not become one was largely attributable to the concern of his school-teacher. Her dedication to her task and her willingness to accept help and professional support carried her and her pupil through stress and crisis. Difficulties at school had to be dealt with without any clear understanding of the family conflict, or its psychopathology. Mrs. Taylor's patience and caring were part of her teacher's role. She did not become a therapist nor Tommy a patient. But, by accepting and working through her own painful conflicts, she enabled Tommy to deal with his.

CHAPTER 11

WORKING TOGETHER : CARING AND COLLABORATING

IN this book discussion has centred on what can be done to help people in trouble — clients, patients, parishioners, pupils or neighbours. Terms like 'crisis intervention' and 'counselling' have been used, rather than 'case-work' or 'psychotherapy', to emphasize that the handling of crisis situations does not necessarily demand training of a highly sophisticated nature. Evidence abounds to show that a person can be helped by another's concern, by the expression of an accepting and caring interest. It is this human warmth which is important and which may, in emergencies, prove to be life-saving. However, concern in itself may not be enough.

In the first three chapters the basic principles of crisis intervention are outlined, and the case-histories contained in subsequent chapters describe how they operate (or fail to operate) in practice. The intention is to persuade the many non-psychiatrists who are in daily contact with people in trouble not to withdraw because of a sense of personal or professional inadequacy. In the face of another's trouble we are all, to some extent, inadequate. The wise man recognizes his limitations without being so inhibited by them that he makes no move to help. Of course it is sensible, and it gives encouragement and a feeling of security, if the relatively unskilled have colleagues of greater experience to whom they may turn for advice and consultation. In these circumstances there is an opportunity for all to learn together — the individual in trouble, the intervener, and the professional consultant.

The professional relationship

What the consultant or resource person has which the untrained lacks or possesses in less degree is the ability to understand and deal with people professionally. In the field of mental health the relevant quality or skill consists largely of what has been called 'psychodynamic awareness'. This is a difficult term to define. It seems to depend on the willingness and ability to enter into a relationship with another person and understand what is happening emotionally as well as intellectually. In a discussion of the meaning of 'emotional understanding', the Balints[30] have given a simple and telling example. They cite the experience of parents at the arrival of their first baby. This is a happy occasion for most, but in fact is often also worrying and even sometimes alarming. The parents turn to books or doctors for advice in understanding their child and the problems he presents. Often they derive little help. The parents feel that straightforward answers exist to their puzzling problems and may consequently become annoyed because the answers are not forthcoming. Or they may feel that they themselves are to blame in some way and are failing their child. But gradually it dawns on them that what they must do is to get to know their baby better. Reluctantly but inevitably they come to accept that the problems of child-rearing have no simple answers. They are the problems of a close human relationship.

The very words which are customarily used by those caught up in the crises of human behaviour indicate the myths we all tend to perpetuate. The words 'problem' and 'answer' are more appropriate to mathematics than to the experience of parenthood or a psychotherapeutic relationship. But by such expressions we continue to suggest that professionals like doctors, social workers, and clergymen can offer (if only they would) simple answers to life's complex problems. It would be wise of the helping professions to be more forthright in exploding this myth and making plain their role and their limitations in such circumstances. It seems that, disillusioned with the Church, people under stress turned to psychiatry as the new priesthood. Finding few answers and insufficient solace in that quarter either, they have now elected the social worker as answer-man, universal social expert, and problem-remover. The hard truth seems to be that everyone has to deal with his own problems. It is we ourselves who must accept responsibility for our personal difficulties and all we can reasonably expect is understanding and help in working and living through them. The degree and quality of help, how it is given, and why and when, are matters which are the concern of psychotherapy. This is the approach, the subject-matter, and the essential nature of crisis-intervention, counselling, and case-work.

Until recently only a minority of psychiatrists ventured outside their clinics or consulting-rooms to collaborate with colleagues in other disciplines. Even now, when collaboration and mutual understanding is more common, there is a tendency to distinguish between what psychiatrists do and what social workers, psychiatric nurses, or lay therapists do. The implication is that the therapy given by a psychiatrist must be, by that very fact, better, more skilled, and more effective. Even within the discipline of psychiatry itself there exists a prejudice that psychoanalysts alone have the necessary 'letters patent' which confer the real knowledge and privilege of the 'talking treatment'. Again the implication is that other kinds of psychotherapy are second-best. While it would not be difficult to find individual examples to support or disprove such implications, the argument itself is fruitless and destructive.

In a discussion of the place of psychoanalysis in the provision of psychotherapeutic services to the community, Sutherland[31] has this to say. 'It would be universally agreed that the kind of therapeutic work that a social caseworker or other professional helper can carry out appropriately does not attempt what the psychoanalyst does. This limitation need not be further considered because what is normally attempted by others has its own validity as well as being so often the only help available. It must, however, be admitted that the attitudes sometimes conveyed by psychoanalysts that this kind of work is a poor substitute for what more thoroughgoing analysis might achieve, is more a professional fantasy than an established fact. For many, psychological help, and particularly in crisis situations, is probably best given by the kind of relationship the good social or other professional worker can make — one in which the whole person with his own resources and those of his life space are kept firmly as the focus of concern.' If one adds the point made by Thompson and Kahn[32] that it is increasingly being recognized that different methods at different levels are appropriate to different circumstances, then the controversy is put into appropriate perspective.

The demand for help and the need for co-operation

Any survey of community mental health which includes an examination of goals, programmes of action, the scope for preventive measures, and the resources available, reveals the immensity of the task. One of the objectives of a community mental health programme must be the building-up and the extension of skilled psychotherapeutic help. There is already a perceptible movement in this direction. It is worthwhile to consider briefly some proposals for encouraging this movement.

Already mentioned has been the tendency of the expert to isolate himself. It almost seems, as Sutherland[31] has pointed out, that the growth of expertise in a therapeutic method is accompanied by a narrowing of its range of applicability. Patients or clients are not seen or not accepted because they are 'unsuitable'. One result of this has been the springing up of movements like Alcoholics Anonymous, Synanon, and the Samaritans. They have been called into being to fill a gap in the official provision of services; but it may be they do more than this — they utilize methods and pioneer approaches which are novel and innovative. It seems that our present society has never been more aware both of the nature of psychological stress and also the need for suitable intervention. This has led to the birth of a variety of agencies to whom those in distress can turn. This is entirely appropriate and useful. But if these different agencies pursue a lone and separate course, they run a considerable risk of failure. If they are themselves to have the potential for growth and learning, they require to forge close links not only with each other, but also with a centre of specialist knowledge. Any helper or therapist is tempted by his client to move beyond the limits of his own experience and capabilities. For example, the presenting crisis, when examined in more detail, reveals layers of a more complex nature. Does the helper probe further or not? What action does he take in the face of fresh revelations? It is in this kind of situation that the availability of professional consultation proves its value.

With such considerations in mind, the following proposals are made.

1. There already exist in our society centres of psychiatric and psycho-therapeutic expertise. In truth, they may not all be so brimful of expertise as one might wish. However, we must start from where we are. Generally speaking, the psychiatrist trained in psychotherapy provides the highest level of skill available. His colleagues in clinic or hospital provide similar, often less broadly based, psychological understanding and expertise. In the past, such professionals were confined within their institutional walls and tended to work only with individual patients. Nowadays, there is a growing acceptance of the importance of social factors in mental breakdown, the critical place of family and work relationships, and a willingness to use group methods and to move outwith the clinic's confines to treat and consult. This policy would benefit from being more clearly defined and from being given more official and formal support from Area Health Boards and teaching departments.

2. The proliferation of other professional and non-professional helping agencies should be encouraged. The manifestations of psychological disturbance take many forms and help is therefore sought from many different sources and at various levels of need. The physical symptoms of an anxiety state may take the subject to his general practitioner; marital disharmony to the marriage guidance counsellor or the lawyer; delin-

quency to the teacher, policeman or probation officer. At the present time, therefore, many professions and agencies are concerned with those in the throes of personal and family difficulties. They are involved because those in trouble find them available and appropriate. The challenge is whether they can become more appropriate in the sense of becoming more knowledgeable, more relevant, and more effective.

3. The suggestion is not to transmogrify such agencies into psychotherapy clinics or the agents into mini-psychiatrists. One of their present advantages is their acceptability to their clients, which may depend on the fact that they are not labelled 'psychiatric'. Often their work is orientated towards sorting-out family disagreements and dealing with practical living problems. But initial contacts of this kind often lead to the uncovering of more obvious emotional problems which the agent may feel are beyond his capabilities to handle. Here again lies the advantage of a good working relationship with a psychotherapy clinic or other skilled agency which can offer consultation and collaboration.

4. Experience demonstrates that such collaboration sometimes fails because of a lack of understanding of one another's roles, the failure to identify needs and resources, and the inability to construct a broad but acceptable framework within which different approaches can co-exist. Boundary walls between different professions and disciplines still exist and sometimes stand too high for any clear view to be possible of one another's activities. A surprising degree of misinformation and mistrust is thereby fostered. Perhaps the only practical method of dealing with such difficulties is for the specialist centre and the agency concerned to seek a permanent or, at least, long-standing relationship. Learning in the field of psychotherapy is a never-ending process, and it requires an agreed and trustful collaboration over time.

5. Given such a relationship, where collaboration and consultation can take place, there is the opportunity for steady development of psychotherapeutic knowledge and skill. In the example cited earlier of the new parents anxious over their baby, the growth of a more confident acceptance of parenthood and their relationship with the child enabled them to deal with their problems. In a sense they became identified with their child and something of this process occurs in any psychotherapeutic relationship. But the professional learns not only to become involved but also to be objective. His conduct is determined, as far as possible, by the client's perceived needs. This is a rather different situation from

the parent–child relationship, although it may repeat or mimic many features of it. The therapists's own personal interests and emotions require to be carefully monitored, and his role is not to perpetuate the relationship but to bring it to a successful end with the client's completion of the agreed task. This sort of relationship and transaction is in fact complex and likely to be disturbing to both parties. The skills involved in handling it therapeutically are not to be derived from books or lectures. They are more likely to be learned from actual practice, particularly with the supervision and consultation of skilled psychotherapists.

One model the author has found useful is that of the multi-disciplinary team, particularly when involved in a therapeutic community setting.[33] In this situation relatively unskilled staff are given an atmosphere of encouragement and support in which mistakes can be made and learned from, relationship difficulties worked through, and personal change suitably effected. What has been demonstrated over a period of years is that undergraduate and postgraduate students of medicine, social work, occupational therapy, nursing and theology, as well as practising family doctors, clergymen, prison officers, probation officers, psychiatrists and others can share a common and fundamental learning experience which enhances their psychotherapeutic effectiveness.

It is likely that any psychiatric centre which is willing to accept such responsibilities, in addition to those of a more direct service to patients, will become the hub of a related series of mental health agencies serving the whole community. But, in this enterprise, psychiatrists are wise to avoid any suggestion that they are 'taking-over' or that their professional status confers unassailable rights. Whatever the benefits of the 'medical model' of treatment, on which hospital-based psychiatrists have cut their teeth, the so-called 'social-model' may be altogether more appropriate in the many cases dealt with by community-based agencies. Instead of removing the individual to the artificial environment of hospital to be dealt with by experts (a manoeuvre which in certain circumstances is appropriate and sometimes life-saving) he is retained in his family and community, whose natural resources the helper seeks to mobilize and co-ordinate. In this field psychiatrists have still much to learn.

It is evident that the growth of an effective and co-ordinated community mental health service depends on the formation of new relationships across disciplines and institutions. The challenge to the various professions concerned is how far are they willing to go in revising their concepts and modifying their accustomed roles and boundaries. The following pages take a look at the characteristics and preoccupations of the relevant professions.

CHAPTER 12

THE PROFESSIONALS

1. The Family Doctor

IN Britain the National Health Service ensures that almost everyone is on the list of a general practitioner. There is therefore ready access, and no financial barrier, to medical care. This state of affairs, understandably, raises its own problems. A small number of patients, by thoughtless or selfish use of the Service, have raised doubts in the minds of almost all medical practitioners about the nature of doctor–patient relationships, the effect of the Welfare State upon individual responsibility, and the status and rewards of medical practice. Nevertheless, the wide benefits which the N.H.S. has brought the general population far outweigh its disadvantages. Of particular moment is the ready availability of general and specialist care to the whole population. In addition the N.H.S. is now organized with the intent of co-ordinating hospital and community agencies. This provides a suitable framework for the elaboration of comprehensive community mental health services.

Two recent reports[34,35] give information about the general practitioner's work and the kinds of patients who consult him. It appears that approximately half his patients have minor illnesses of a non-specific nature. Major illnesses like coronary thrombosis, pneumonia, or cancer are comparatively rare, presenting perhaps once in a week. For the rest his cases are evenly divided between minor specific ailments (such as hayfever) chronic disorders (like rheumatism) and what has been termed 'social pathology'. The latter includes problems of family life, mental subnormality, and alcoholism. The typical family doctor in Britain sees about two-thirds of his patients at least once a year. He does some 150 consultations per week, a fifth of them in the patient's home. Over the period of a year, from a practice list of 2500 patients, he is likely to meet 360 episodes of mental disorder, more than half of which are neurotic in nature.

For long there has been agreement that many of the complaints which people bring to their doctors originate in emotional disturbance. Figures in the literature vary widely, no doubt because of the prejudices and different approaches of the doctors and investigators concerned, but an accepted estimate is 25 to 30 per cent of all patients consulting a family physician. If one supposes that the so-called 'minor, non-specific ailments' and those labelled 'social pathology' conceal a significant number of emotionally disturbed patients who may be added to the 25 per cent of those more clearly identified as psychologically disordered, then the large size of the problem is evident. Yet it is no secret that general practice, by and large, has been shy of accepting responsibility for this aspect of its task. All too often the busy practitioner attempts to escape from such patients behind a barricade of prescriptions for tranquillizers, hypnotics, and anti-depressants. Not that there is no proper place for such medication. Certainly the wise physician, once he has acquainted himself with the patient and the disorder, will make use of such resources as seem helpful and available, including the benefits of medication. But our age seems to be characterized by a zealous and unrealistic dependence on drugs of one kind and another. Stevens,[36] a general practitioner, writing on the use of hypnotics in sleeplessness, comments: 'Few human beings are averse to taking drugs, many doctors enjoy prescribing them and most nurses like giving them. It is, therefore, no wonder that millions of patients proceed on a long succession of nightly chemical "trips" which bring them less and less comfort as time goes on.' It is unreasonable to expect that the anxieties and depressions of human life, which are inescapable features of developmental and accidental crises, can be usefully met by pills and capsules. Before reaching for the prescription-pad even the busiest doctor might ask the anxious, depressed, or insomniac patient the question 'why?' and sometime take pause to hear the answer.

In Western countries there has been a general change-over in recent years to group practices, night-call services, and week-end rotas. These changes set limits on the concepts of a personal family physician and continuity of care. The alteration in hospital practice is also striking, with nurses, doctors and paramedical staff working in shifts and in teams. Lost in the crowd, half-hidden by piles of laboratory test-results, does the patient still have the opportunity to form a personal relationship with his physician?

The general practitioner, as the doctor of first contact, has at least the opportunity of seeing his patient whole, psyche and soma together, in the family context. He has a difficult task and time is at a premium. The busy surgery, the list of calls which await, render the listening ear less receptive. Yet his talent must be to sense what lies at the heart of the matter and to do so quickly. The demand is that he be versatile and capable of dealing with a wide range of disorders occurring in a variety of settings. It is small wonder that many general practitioners, in such circumstances, retreat from the demands of anything resembling a psychotherapeutic relationship, use medicaments uncritically, or consign a steady stream of patients to other agencies.

An interesting survey was conducted some years ago by May and Gregory.[37] Its main aim was to discover how far the general practitioners in one locality were prepared to participate in the care of psychiatric patients. The findings indicated a general indifference to psychiatry and little awareness or enthusiasm for the role suggested for the G.P. by the Ministry of Health; that is, that he should encourage early recognition of psychiatric illness and act as co-ordinator of the team providing clinical and social care in the community. The authors commented: 'At present the G.P.'s concept of his role is one of detachment from the organization and operation of specialist psychiatric services, and until general practice undergoes some reorganization in its methods of training and its relation with hospital and local authority services it is unrealistic to expect any more from it.' Since these words were written, far-reaching changes have taken place and are in process both in the training of general practitioners and also in their working relationships with other branches of the N.H.S. How fully these changes are presently encouraging and fitting G.P.s for a fuller role in community mental health it is difficult to say.

The present writer feels that without a full participation by the G.P., there is little chance that mental health services can be other than lop-sided and inefficient. The hope is that, as psychiatric personnel themselves show a greater willingness to consult and treat outside their institutions, as the opportunity grows for collaboration in health centres, and as social worker and health visitor attachments to general practice become universal, so family doctors will be stimulated to accept their key role in community mental health.

2. The Social Worker

In the mental health field the social worker was generally considered to be that member of the treatment team who was concerned and knowledgeable about environmental factors. She was the one who knew the patient's family background, his job, and his financial situation. Partly because many social workers were poorly trained to perform other functions, and partly because of medical autocracy, ignorance, and exclusiveness, social workers were restricted to a minor therapeutic role. In the traditional mental hospital, for example, the psychiatric social worker's main task was to interview patients' relatives and prepare a social background report. This was filed in the case-notes and sometimes was even read by the psychiatrist treating the patient. The P.S.W. might also be asked to help to disentangle a muddle of hire-purchase debts, or intercede with the appropriate authorities over housing, National Insurance contributions, or pension rights. But it was unusual for her to be involved in any formal psychotherapeutic relationship. Probably her nearest approach would be in follow-up visits to a discharged patient in his own home. There she might feel free enough of the restrictions of her hospital role to engage in a therapeutic relationship. Some social workers — in particular those who had gained formal training in mental health — overcame these restrictive practices. They sought to apply their knowledge to individuals and families, engaging in long-term relationships with the object of changing attitudes and behaviour. Unfortunately, some of these 'case-workers' adopted a diluted or distorted version of psychoanalytic theory and method. In such circumstances they needed exceptional gifts to be of benefit to their clients and also able to survive personally themselves. However, recent years have seen rapid changes in methods of training and in treatment orientations. The team structure of child psychiatry has always allowed a full therapeutic role for the trained social worker. Also, the growing acceptance of the concepts of the therapeutic community and the multi-disciplinary team model has encouraged the expansion of treatment roles for non-medical workers generally, including the social worker. It was thus possible in many areas for P.S.W.'s to operate as experts in their own field and as valued partners in a treatment team.

In Britain this natural progress was interrupted by the introduction of new legislation and by fundamental changes in professional organizations, in particular the rapid growth of local authority social service departments. The Children and Young Persons Act of 1969, and the Local Authority Social Services Act of 1970, brought many different social workers together in one department. The Seebohm Report ushered in this era, with notions of generic training and an all-purpose social worker. The suggestion was made that the multifarious needs and complaints, which previously had taken individuals to a variety of agencies, were basically expressions of family pathology and that one department should take entire responsibility for them. Such a brave ambition must evoke admiration. However, to date, its attempted realization has provoked many difficulties, some administrative convulsions, and not a little chaos. Social service departments are currently engaged in rethinking and modifying their original premises and plans. Kahn,[38] pointing out that no unified theory was in existence to support these original far-reaching ambitions, says: 'Social workers cannot, any more than doctors, carry sufficient knowledge in one person to deal with such a variety of problems. Even though the staff of different departments have been brought together, some of the old skills remain obstinately separate, and new comprehensive skills have yet to be developed.'

Whatever the eventual consequences of these changes – and the present writer believes they will be advantageous – the confusion and ineptitude which immediately followed their introduction invited severe criticism. Even now some of the more imaginative measures may forfeit general acceptance, for example, the abolition of juvenile courts and their replacement by diagnostic and treatment services for children in trouble. Criticism is justifiably directed at any procedures which sweep away familiar methods and resources while failing to replace them with adequate substitutes.

There remains a clear need for an improved quality and quantity of staff in local authority departments, staff who are appropriately trained, adequately supervised, and satisfied enough by their work that they are not constantly in transit. Most directors of social work have abandoned any strict adherence to the concept of the generic social worker, recognizing the urgent need for the development of special skills. 'Psychodynamic awareness' is certainly one of these and it is to be regretted that mental health training is not set at a higher level of priority and status than it seems to be in many local authority departments. At the same time, it may be appropriate for social workers to define their tasks and boundaries a little more precisely. Any social work department is set to fail if it accepts as its concern everything which happens to land on its doorstep. There must surely be a dividing line between the responsibility of one profession and another and between the responsibility of the social worker and society as a whole. The developed and necessary skills of the social worker require to be used intelligently and economically. All too often they seem to be spread thinly, used idiosyncratically, or in unnecessary isolation. The social worker with mental health training is a professional whose close working links with hospitals, general practice, welfare services, schools, and courts of law, put her in a central position in the community. She it is who can respond appropriately to crises, who can give both direct service and also stimulate and facilitate other agencies, exploiting more imaginatively the resources of the community itself. But she cannot do it all by herself. A closer working relationship with other disciplines, particularly in the psychiatric services, must precede any worthwhile advance.

3. The Probation Officer

While in England and Wales the Probation Officer retains a separate identity, in Scotland the Social Work Act of 1968 brought him into the same department as other social workers. Thus there is no separate probation service in Scotland. This has led to the criticism that the duties previously performed by skilled probation officers (for example, court reports and the supervision of offenders) are now in the hands of inexperienced social workers and their performance suffers thereby. There is no doubt that such criticism has been justified; but as already stated, there is now an acceptance of the need for special skills and the differentiation of social work skills, so that this particular problem is likely to be solved by the passage of time.

Criminologists and social reformers have for long been critical of the penal system and have strongly recommended that imprisonment of offenders should be a last resort in the vast majority of cases. This view has come to be accepted in recent times and the Criminal Justice Act of 1972 emphasized the importance of treatment in the community. It supported a wider use of probation and of day training centres, community service orders, and bail hostels. Young offenders, who represent a large slice of all those convicted of indictable crimes, provide special problems. There has always been a proper reluctance to consign young people to prison and probation orders have been used most frequently with this age group. Research studies have demonstrated that supervision in the community produces results which are at least no worse than custodial methods; and there is a recommendation from the Home Office Advisory Council on the Penal System[39] that detention centres, borstals, and young offenders institutions be abolished. To a large extent they might be replaced by supervision and control orders enforced by the probation and aftercare service. It seems somewhat paradoxical that, while such reports are being published on the one hand, on the other there is in Britain a detailed commitment to a massive and costly prison building programme. It is difficult to see how a vigorous and innovative departure into non-custodial measures will succeed under the auspices of prison departments bound to the ethos of locks and high walls.

It is clear nevertheless that society is concerned about the nature and incidence of crime and how it is dealt with. It would be folly to suppose that deviant behaviour, the roots of which go deep into the values and practices of our society, will respond to simple measures or new 'treatments'. Our unstable materialistic society with its injustices and assaults on individuality, our culture which generates violence, drug-dependence, and emotional stress, must discover within itself the seeds of its own salvation. Certainly there can be no expectation that the task of dealing with offenders can be simply delegated to probation officers, children's panels, or psychiatrists. Society gets the criminals it deserves. However, the present climate may be suitable for fresh and experimental ventures in this field and probation officers will be involved in both planning and implementing new methods. It would be wise to recognize the honest doubts expressed by magistrates, police, and others regarding the effectiveness of children's panels, current criticism of a system which emphasizes 'help' rather than 'justice', and the very real difficulties of handling certain disturbed offenders outside a secure residential institution. Certainly the availability of suitable resources in terms of skilled personnel and facilities is of vital importance. Despite all such considerations, however, it seems that the probation officer is now being given the opportunity of enlarging his traditional role of 'advising, assisting, and befriending'. He will meet such a challenge successfully only with a full measure of understanding and support from other disciplines and from the general public itself.

4. The Schoolteacher

One cannot write about schools and teachers without some consideration of what education is for. The question seems so obvious, and yet many current difficulties spring from our inability to give to it a clear and acceptable reply. Few would disagree that our educational system needs some measure of reform, although some would go much further than others. But what should schools be like? What should be taught, and how, and why? How far might it prove possible to use the educational system quite deliberately to improve the mental health of our communities?

These are large questions and cannot be discussed here at any length. But it would be foolish to ignore how the values of our society must affect, and be affected by, the purposes of our educational institutions, wherein our children spend such a large part of their formative years. As Silberman[40] has affirmed, 'education is inescapably a moral as well as an intellectual and aesthetic enterprize. But talking about morality, honesty, or kindness in no way ensures that people will act morally, honestly, or kindly. The job of the educator is to teach in such a way as to convert "ideas about morality" into "moral ideas".'

In no way does this deny the importance of imparting to pupils academic knowledge or intellectual skills. Young people are not likely to have much self-respect and independence if they cannot master appropriate skills in reading, writing, and calculation. Indeed the two aspects of learning – the intellectual and the social – go hand in hand. This point seems to be poorly understood by schoolteachers who complain endlessly that they cannot do their jobs because of lack of discipline in the classroom. An inappropriate curriculum and an outmoded teaching system may go far in explaining why many working-class children fail to learn; and it is their own sense of failure which produces behaviour problems, in and out of school. But curricular reform of itself cannot have a far-reaching effect without changes in the school's social system – the way the school is organized and the way teachers teach. Despite the real advances of the past few decades, it is still impossible to visit schools without noting petty and oppressive rules governing staff as well as pupils, a general lack of openness and civility, and an absence of spontaneity and creativity in the processes of learning and self-discovery.

Despite the findings of social scientists on the importance of social structure in any institution of learning, and despite the demonstrations of psychiatrists and other workers – including educationists themselves – of the dynamics of groups, 'open systems', and their application to learning, most schools have chosen to ignore this knowledge. In Britain the word 'progressive' is almost a term of abuse when applied to an educational establishment; and there remains an alarming degree of misunderstanding of, and aversion to, new methods with a corresponding reliance on traditional social structure and inflexible discipline. It is an exaggeration to suggest that schools are part of the country's custodial system, but many of them fall far short of being 'academies of self-realization.'

Teaching in most countries is an ill-paid profession. It has its quota of timeservers who have fallen into the job rather than been attracted to it from a sense of vocation. But, for its own part, society must make up its mind what it wants of its educators; and it stands a better chance of obtaining it if teachers are rewarded more worthily. Perhaps, before we can educate our children wisely, we need first to educate parents and teachers! This paradox serves to remind us once again of the limits set on the 'expert' or the 'professional' and how important is the influence of informed public opinion. This in turn is often in the hands of the 'hidden educators' – mainly those of press, cinema, and television – whose motives may not always be in the public interest. The teacher then has a difficult task. Society asks him to inculcate in the child a sense of tradition, to socialize him and produce a conforming citizen, to give him knowledge of the past and also to open his mind to the new. Eiseley[41] writes: 'The teacher stands as interpreter and disseminator of both tradition and innovation. . . . He must fight with circumstances for the developing mind. . . . His lot is worse than sculptors in snow – he is a sculptor of the intangible future.'

In the U.S.A. for some time past and in Britain more recently there has existed a system of guidance and counselling in schools. Evidently this development derived more from social, economic, and political pressures than from purely educational ones. Perhaps the main function of counselling to date has been to focus attention on the pupil as a whole person whose emotional status affects his capacity to learn. Such a development is, in a way, a tacit admission of the previous failure of schools to teach children how to live. The main danger now may be the assumption that the appointment of guidance teachers in a school takes care of the whole problem and permits all other teachers to concentrate on the preparation for examinations. They may feel it inappropriate to accept opportunities for interactions with their pupils in anything other than the subjects they teach, and thus will fail to capitalize on the everyday 'living-learning' situations thrown up in class.

The advent of the guidance teacher, nevertheless, signals the opportunity for new departures in pedagogy and for an expansion of methods which good schools have for long been practising. Certain features of our society and our educational system make this advance a matter of urgency. Craft[42] has argued the case cogently and some of his points may be briefly stated. It is to be expected that a democratic society will show concern for the underprivileged and the appointment of school counsellors – along with school social workers and other specialists – gives the opportunity for personal counselling with pupils and parents who have no previous experience of extended education. As schools become larger, more complex, and more impersonal, there is need for someone to guide and to provide globality of concern. In society's state of advanced industrialization there is a need for adaptability in the labour force – a quality that may now be more important than the 'hard work' which most teachers still insist upon. It may be that guidance and counselling in schools is relevant to the increasing need in society for adaptability and technical skill, assuming that such teaching encourages self-awareness, maturity, and flexibility. It is appropriate for the guidance teacher to identify talents and aptitudes and help to tailor courses to particular profiles of abilities, culminating in sound vocational guidance. But education is more than simply talent production and the goal is that of an enriched life for the individual. There are greater truths than can be written on the blackboard.

It is likely that a large proportion of counselling will be 'crisis counselling', particularly at the start of such a service or in the case of schools in disadvantaged neighbourhoods. Often the crisis will be one of a series and other agencies will already be involved — for example, probation officer, social worker, child psychiatrist, or educational psychologist. As the counselling service develops, crisis intervention should become less necessary since changes will have taken place within the social structure of the school. Hopefully these will lead to better communication between departments and teachers, and also between pupils and teachers; encourage an increase in *shared* decision-making, which involves not only junior teachers and pupils, but also parents; and thus occasion a growing acceptance that the school belongs to its community, who can and should support it and use it as a community resource.

At the present time a large source of energy, which might be utilized in schools, goes abegging. It is the deep and enduring concern which the vast majority of parents have for their children. If schools, parents, and children could look together at their needs and resources, it might light up whole neighbourhoods.

5. The Clergyman

Any clergyman not lost in the rosy glow of his stained-glass windows must be concerned over the present position of the Church in contemporary society. It appears to have too many empty buildings, too many empty dogmas, and not enough members. It is accused of giving little in the way of leadership and, even when it does, of being reactionary or irrelevant. People think of the Church as always saying 'Thou shalt not' rather than as encouraging positive and fulfilling effort. It is often felt to be traditional and defensive when it might be experimental and creative.

Yet it was the Church which provided the original source of care and welfare and it still plays an important part in this direction. It runs old-folks homes, youth clubs, and other institutions for those who are sick or in need. Its support and influence underlie many worthwhile community organizations and projects. However, its more lively clergymen and members remain dissatisfied and are engaged in a search for a fuller pastoral role and a more relevant place in society.

In a report delivered to the Church of Scotland General Assembly in 1971 . and called *Keeping Pace with Tomorrow*[43] a number of themes and problems are discussed and recommendations offered. The statement is made: 'That the Church must be on the move forward we take to be self-evident simply because the Church of Jesus Christ *is mission* and the Church's Lord is always on ahead of his people calling them in missionary obedience and faithfulness to keep pace with tomorrow.' One applauds the sentiment but wonders whether the very terms in which it is couched provide one reason why so many who are by no means unsympathetic to the Church become impatient with it. In this report, the current malaise of the Church is acknowledged. One criticism made is that present congregations are both too small and too large to be effective. It is suggested therefore that larger co-operative units – a kind of area church – might be formed while, at the same time, small groups of members would embark on particular lines of endeavour. In seeking to work out 'a strategy for engaging the world on all fronts' the report emphasizes that 'for theology and faith to retreat out of politics and social struggle, for instance, and into the purely private dimensions is tantamount to conceding the field to purely secular powers.' The report identifies the areas of priority as industry, education, the mass media, and politics. A tall order.

Mills, who is Director of Counselling Development and Training in the Church of Scotland, has this to say:[44] 'Amid the cry for new structures in the church today the individual in his needs and in his relationships must remain central. One way of ensuring this is to re-discover the power of the caring group.' One of Dr. Mills' criticisms of church groups is that they are busy *doing* things rather than reaching out to people in need. He points to the familiar church organizations – Woman's Guild, Men's Club, Youth Fellowship, Choir, Boys' Brigade, Sunday School Teachers' Group – all of which fulfil valid and important functions. But what churches lack are *caring* groups which are prepared to meet people at the point of their anxiety and despair. He cites those who are afflicted by alcoholism, drug dependency, personality disorders, and psychological and spiritual problems; and he underlines the need for care to prevent their falling into crisis situations and for skilled help if they do. 'I believe that help is available in every parish. We require to identify it. We require to organize it, to make it available. We require to encourage it, to increase its understanding, insights and skills.' There are in most parishes members who possess relevant skills and have a contribution to make in the education of groups which seek to further this particular task of the Church. Indeed it might well be accepted as an important function of the clergyman that he gives a lead to his congregation in identifying resources within and without his parish and organizes groups of this nature.

Canon Burnett[45] supports such a view, recommending the study and understanding of group dynamics as a way of furthering the life and work of the Church. He quotes McCaughey on the subject: 'God comes to a man where he is . . . we start with our questions, our preoccupations . . . it is only as we live firmly embedded in the reality of our own world that we can hear speaking to us the God of the Bible. . . . Study is an offering we make to God. . . . It probably will hurt; we must study, as used to be said, until we have "a pain in the mind".'

If the Church stands for anything in our world today it stands for love. Fletcher[46] points out that the radical obligation of the Christian ethic is to love one's neighbour whether one likes him or not. The love being urged in the prescriptions, 'Thou shalt love thy neighbour as thyself', and 'Love your enemies', is not the love of friendship, romance, sentiment, or affection. Rather it is the requirement to deal lovingly with one another and, even more, offer 'tender loving care' whether there is any return of affection or not. In the throes of their crisis, wrapped up in anxiety or distress, people in trouble are often demanding and selfish. It is just when they are most unlovable that such people need this kind of love most urgently. So, whether we are Christians or not, church-members or not, there may be something for all care-givers to recognize in this fundamental moral duty.

As has been suggested earlier, the clergyman, by the very nature of his calling, is in daily contact with illness, distress, and bereavement. Moreover he has a particular opportunity of counselling the young, those proposing marriage within the Church, and the elderly (who seem to comprise the majority of many a congregation). In the past, the clergyman often avoided his opportunities, escaping into moral exhortation, prayer, or theological jargon which had little meaning for his listeners. However, there is now a growing awareness of the significance and virtue of counselling, which – in its principles of listening empathetically and without judgment – echoes all religious concern for healing and personal integration. This kind of role for the clergyman is clearly important. To fulfil it adequately in church and community he may have first to face the challenge of new experiences in training, group relationships, and social action. It is unlikely that he can keep pace with tomorrow in any other way.

6. The Nurse

(i) *The psychiatric nurse.*

In former times becoming a hospital nurse was a cross between entering a nunnery and joining a guard's regiment. Life was characterized by long hours of duty, unquestioning dedication, poor food, small financial reward, and a vow of obedience. In some respects the resemblance may be thought to persist. However, as in many other disciplines, rapid change is evident. To date this has been most clearly seen in mental hospitals, where fundamental alterations in organization and function have brought new opportunities to the psychiatric nurse.

The present writer[47] suggested sometime ago that psychiatric nursing had arrived at important cross-roads: 'There lies ahead a wide opportunity of service and fulfilment or else a steadily diminishing professional role.' On the one hand a path could be discerned which led to better training, more professional status, and an expanding treatment role outside hospital as well as within it. In the opposite direction, another road led back into outmoded customs and defences, towards dwindling responsibility and status, where active therapy was the prerogative of other professions and the nurse was confined to caring for the psychogeriatric or the chronic insane. Happily the challenge of a new professionalism appears to have been accepted by most psychiatric nurses who, if at first anxiously and grudgingly, are now willing to revise and expand their functions. In particular they are demonstrating their skill and knowledge in dealing with the mentally disordered outside the hospital walls. The advent of the community psychiatric nurse signals a significant advance.

Few observers would doubt that the main resources of mental health skill reside at present in psychiatric hospitals and clinics. It is there that staff of different kinds (psychiatrists, clinical psychologists, social workers, and nurses) have built up their knowledge by caring for individuals with severe mental disturbance and by engaging in treatment relationships with a variety of patients over long periods of time. This reservoir of skill and experience lay relatively untapped until recently. In the case of the psychiatric nurse, it was mainly the reluctance of her own hierarchy which prevented her escaping from the hospital fastness to work with colleagues in out-patient clinics or engage in domiciliary treatment and follow-up. However, as emphasis upon community mental health grew and hospital linkages with outside agencies became stronger, so the psychiatric nurse became accustomed, as part of the clinical team, to accompany social worker and psychiatrist into new areas of commitment. Indeed, in some respects, the nurse has outstripped her colleagues in psychiatry and social work by the ease with which she has established contact and found common ground with non-psychiatric agencies. She has given a clear indication of her value in out-patient clinics, follow-up visiting, consultation to schools and old folks' homes, and in collaboration with the general practice team. Examples now abound of how the particular skills of the psychiatric nurse may be used to advantage – see, for example, the accounts of Stobie and Hopkins,[48] and Henderson and his colleagues.[49]

Despite such stimulating examples, however, prejudices and restrictive practices continue within the nursing profession and hamper its advance. Similar attitudes may also be evident in the relationship between other professionals and the nurse. It seems likely that the psychiatric nurse has been constrained for so long in a system which devalued and suppressed her therapeutic contribution, that she needs time and encouragement before she can assume new responsibilities with full confidence. The support of a multidisciplinary team structure will not only help her to recognize and apply appropriate skills, but also give her the opportunity of sharing her knowledge and experience with colleagues in other disciplines.

This is an example of a support-system which is necessary for the well-being of any professional worker, in or out of hospital. It is foolish to encourage anyone to abandon the familiar, if somewhat rigid, structure of the traditional mental hospital for an isolated role in the community. Without the opportunity for discussion of problems and mutual understanding and support, any helping-agent will become stressed and stranded, and run the risk of breakdown. It is remarkable how long it has taken mental health workers to recognize this need and respond to it appropriately. Perhaps the planned expansion of health centres in Britain will offer a suitable meeting-place where different disciplines – including the mental health nurse – can resolve their mistrusts and misunderstandings, achieve good working relationships, and face together the challenges of 'front-line' practice.

(ii) *The health visitor*

Health visiting is now a prestigious nursing specialty. But the first health visitors were not trained nurses at all. In fact they were working-class women who were chosen and employed to help poor and ignorant mothers bring up their families. It was hoped in this way to reduce the then disastrously high infant mortality rate and also alleviate the poor nutrition of young children living in neglected and over-crowded conditions. In the 1920s it came to be recognized that such work demanded not only goodwill and common sense, but also knowledge of hygiene, nutrition, and child-rearing. Subsequently therefore health visiting became a specialty of nursing, aiming to prevent disease and promote healthy development in children.

Although conditions in our society have changed greatly and health visiting has also changed, it is evident that the history of this nursing specialty continues to exert an undue influence on its practice. In the present corps of health visitors – although this seems less true of younger members – there is a preoccupation with physical factors and a suspicion of psychological explanations. Sometimes there is a clear failure to understand the opportunities which are offered by the role of health visitor in dealing with the ills of a total family group. The health visitor sees the child as her only responsibility; consequently she has been known to describe an unhappy marriage and the disruptive behaviour of the husband as none of her concern. It may be that health visitors still fail to enjoy a full enough training in mental health and consequently feel unable to deal with the psychosocial crises which threaten individuals and families.

Many health visitors are now attached to G.P.'s rather than to geographical areas. They have already become highly valued members of the health team, although, in some practices, there has occurred a jostling for position in the status stakes. The health visitor has been heard to complain at times that the family doctor devalues her comments or ignores her recommendations; and it is not a matter of chance that this happens most in the field of mental health, where both are least certain of their expertise.

In 1965 it was estimated that the health visitor spent 57 per cent of her time in travelling, 27 per cent in administration, and only 16 per cent in actual patient care. The practice now is for her to play a large part in the care of children, new mothers, and the elderly; and these patients are often seen in her own regular 'surgeries'. It seems entirely right and proper that a highly qualified professional like the health visitor should combine her interest in preventive medicine and health supervision with an expanding treatment role. There is still scope for experiment in finding a suitable structure for the primary care team. As an important member of it, the health visitor can help in this endeavour. What is being suggested here is that an ability to find her way with competence through the intricacies of physical, psychological, and social interactions, would put her in the position of making an unique contribution to family welfare.

7. The Policeman

The police service in Britain came into being at the start of the nineteenth century. Rowen and Mayne, who have been described as the founding fathers of the Metropolitan Police, affirmed in 1829 that 'the primary object of an efficient Police is the prevention of crime: the next that of detection of offenders'. But they also went on to say: 'Every member of the force must remember that his duty is to protect and help members of the public no less than to apprehend guilty persons.' It has become apparent that the helping duty now comprises a large proportion of police work.

There have been comparatively few sociological studies of the police; and the picture most of us have, built up on the basis of films, television, and news-stories, may be quite unrealistic. To most people it comes as a surprise to discover just how much of a 'service' as opposed to a law-enforcing function policemen perform. An American study by Cummings[50] showed that more than half the routine calls to the police involved demands for personal help of one kind or another. Punch and Naylor[51] conducted an investigation in Essex, England, and showed that a variation existed between the practice in urban and rural areas. Seventy-three per cent of telephone calls to the police in a 'country town' were classed as service requests compared with 49 per cent in a 'new town'. Figures for the whole survey area revealed that 59 per cent of calls were service requests and 41 law enforcement. Cain[52] in her study of the policeman's role, pointed out that the police are subject to conflicting expectations. She emphasized how important were community structure, police organization, the policeman's own interpretation of his task, and also his view of particular subgroups within the population. Her description of the policeman's routine in both city and country areas demonstrated considerable differences in role definition and performance, and how the factors mentioned play their part. In urban areas it seems clear that the police are themselves more concerned with law enforcement, even although service duties bulk large. In rural areas the policeman appears willing to provide what amounts to a general social service.

The investigation of Punch and Naylor showed that approximately one-third of service requests involved 'domestic occurrences'. These consisted of family disputes, problems of a personal nature, or episodes of disturbance or annoyance. Most service calls were received during normal working hours, which indicates that the police are preferred even when conventional social service departments are open and available. Police reaction to this sizeable burden of welfare duties is (not surprisingly) to feel critical of social service departments. While recognizing the real difficulties such departments face, they describe the police department, a little ironically, as 'the only twenty-four hour fully mobile social service'.[53] This raises what seems to be a reasonable case for naming the social service department, along with police, ambulance, and fire-fighting, the fourth facility in 999 calls.

Such evidence shows that some of the public at least consider the police to be the first-on-call of the social services. They look to a reliable, familiar, and authoritative figure for a quick remedy for their difficulties. Social workers, on the other hand, tend to be seen as airy-fairy theorists who fail to get things done. The police themselves appear to have accepted their role as providing first-aid of a commonsense and humane variety, while being prepared to channel clients to more specialized services. Perhaps less readily they also fulfil a safety-net function — the 'buck-stopping' last resort — for difficult or unpleasant problems which other services, such as probation, welfare, or mental health, cannot or will not handle.

If this picture is indeed the true pattern of the work of police departments, it highlights several points of importance. Firstly, it is clear that the general stereotype of the policeman as the person who spends his time combatting crime is misleading. One wonders why the police have for so long undersold the other aspect of their work and what effect on their public image would be a wider knowledge of their extensive social commitments. Secondly, the question arises: Are our expectations of the policeman's role reasonable? Should he abandon some of these service duties, handing them over explicitly to mental welfare officer, marriage guidance counsellor, or social worker? Thirdly, there comes the obvious question: Given the multifunctional role of the policeman at present, might his training be improved? Would a greater emphasis on sociological and psychological understanding render him a more potent and constructive community agent? Might it, at least, lead to a greater degree of co-operation with other social agencies? Fourthly, there is the possibility of the police themselves setting up more specialized departments. Already in Scotland, following the Social Work Act of 1968, most police forces developed Departments of Community Involvement. Such a specialist department could take notice of the wide spread of service duties which lands on the police doorstep, clarify its own commitments and boundaries, and make realistic arrangements with other agencies in the community.

What is now clearly evident is that the police have long experience of a wide variety of social problems. Their awareness and methods need airing and sharing with other helping agencies.

8. The Lawyer

This particular professional might be cited as an example of someone whose daily round brings him into contact with people in trouble, but who, generally speaking, has made little attempt to acknowledge his wider functions or responsibilities. It would be unkind, and certainly unjustified in the many cases where lawyers are generous of time and effort without reward, to suggest that the legal profession is too busy conveyancing, investing, and advocating to also find time to be caring. Yet such an impression is sometimes given. It is therefore worth recording the recent development of neighbourhood law centres both in the U.S.A. and Britain. Some lawyers became concerned at the large number of the population who could not afford conventional legal advice, or thought they could not, or in any event did not seek such advice. They therefore set up law centres, often in shopping precincts, rather after the fashion of 'walk-in' psychiatric clinics, and attracted a clientele mainly of the poor and underprivileged. Most of their dealings are therefore concerned with disputes over rents, finance companies, evictions, social security benefits, and marital relationships. The need may be measured by the experience of the North Kensington centre, London, which handled an estimated 8000 cases in its first 4 years. Lord Gifford,[54] arguing the case for law centres, said: 'By and large, solicitors are situated in the wrong places, they are open at the wrong time, and their practitioners are expert in the wrong areas of law.' Now, some solicitors at least are in the right place at the right time. But they themselves suggest that many of their clients need social workers as much as lawyers.

It may be that — just like the neighbourhood health centres in the U.S.A. — neighbourhood law centres do their most important work by helping citizens to help themselves. There are few communities that could not benefit from the accumulation of relevant data on current social problems; and encouragement and leadership may be vital for neighbourhood groups to initiate projects, challenge unhelpful regulations, or engage in social action themselves. These are not functions which helping professionals have readily accepted in the past. However, in modern times, the challenge is likely to present itself more and more. The law centre is but one aspect of a wide and sweeping movement in Western society, yet it goes some way to encourage the belief that communities really do care.

Such then are some of the characteristics and preoccupations of the professionals involved in the field of mental health, at least as viewed through one pair of eyes. The presentation is admittedly superficial and oversimplified and there are others concerned with people in trouble who have not been portrayed. Apart from inspectors of cruelty to children, prison officers, mental welfare officers, home-helpers, and so on — who are paid for what they do — there is a veritable army of voluntary workers who serve an important function. The voluntary worker in essence is 'the good neighbour' who often recognizes need where no professional body exists to meet it. Moreover, the voluntary organization can often be experimental and pioneer new approaches when our increasingly bureaucratic institutions are burdened by the dead weight of their own systems and are unable to make the necessary leap forward.

While it is important to distinguish the professional from the voluntary worker, and the trained from the untrained, and while it is well to accept that each has his role, his particular skill, and his boundaries, the constant flux in our society renders anything static something of an obstruction. More than ever before we are being challenged to review our skills and training, and how and where we use them. It seems that professional workers must stay open and alert to new possibilities, new alliances, and new functions. In the field of crisis intervention and community mental health there is unmistakable scope for fresh ideas and more productive co-operation.

CHAPTER 13

PLANNING FOR PROGRESS

THIS book is primarily concerned with psychiatric emergencies, yet one hopes that it is apparent throughout that crisis intervention is not advanced as an isolated treatment method sufficient in itself. While a valuable concept and technique to which more commitment might well be given, crisis intervention, to be of long-term value, must take place within a comprehensive mental health service. Merely to deal with crisis situations, while ignoring underlying causes and longer-term needs, is quite unhelpful. A flexible and comprehensive system, which uses resources in and out of hospital in a discriminating and co-ordinated fashion, directed at the treatment and rehabilitation of the patient and the promotion of community mental health — that is the ideal which is set before us. In such a scheme crisis intervention might be said to be merely a repair shop. But human personalities, unlike automobiles, cannot be scrapped or exchanged for new models. A repair shop therefore is a valuable part of the system. Moreover it may well be in a position to diagnose early, spot recurring troubles, alert other arms of the service, and be in close touch with public needs.

It would be foolish to deny that present mental health services fall short of the ideal sketched above. Indeed they are substantially below what might be achieved on the basis of agreed, existing knowledge. It seems unlikely that there will be a leap forward in this respect without a much keener awareness on the part of the public and a willingness to place more resources in the hands of mental health professionals. Recent years have seen much uninformed criticism of organized psychiatry and severe attacks on mental health workers which would have been better aimed elsewhere. It has been argued, for example, that mental illness is a form of social deviance with which psychiatry deals on behalf of the establishment as a hidden coercive agency. Or that mental disorder is a myth. Some psychiatrists themselves have gone so far as to suggest that only severe mental illness deserves their professional attention and they are critical of colleagues who treat marital disharmony, social discontent, antisocial behaviour, or feelings of general unhappiness. They also express alarm that psychiatrists should feel they have a legitimate role in offering consultation to schools or industrial concerns, labelling such activities as 'psychiatry unlimited'. No doubt amid such criticisms there exists some truth. But, as Eisenberg[55] affirms, 'the fact that psychiatry can be abused does not make psychiatry an abuse'. He further points out that if much of what psychiatrists do is based on little more than codified experience, it is still of benefit to those who suffer, partly by removing the effects of past evils and partly by using new remedies and methods. It is certain that society cannot improve the lot of the mentally ill by projecting blame on psychiatrists and thus attempting to free itself from its own guilts and responsibilities.

Society needs to think hard about these responsibilities. They cannot simply be met by building better psychiatric hospitals nor by emptying the old ones and spilling an army of vulnerable people into a confusing and unwelcoming world. De Tocqueville affirmed nearly 150 years ago: 'What we call necessary institutions are often no more than institutions to which we have grown accustomed.' The mental hospital may well fall into this category. Better treatment methods can be found. But we must try to ensure that they *are* better.

Of course, mental health services cannot exclude themselves from the general social and economic climate. But the economic storms which most countries are currently suffering are but one aspect of the 'unstable state' described by Schon.[56] Such a state of flux gives the opportunity for – perhaps demands – a different sort of planning, one that takes account of new social values. There is presently a revolution in thought directed against economic materialism, uniformity, centralization, and institutional rigidity. Concurrently there is disenchantment with traditional values such as individual achievement, self-control, independence, and endurance. New values are being acclaimed – self-actualization, self-expression, inter-dependence, and capacity for joy.[57] Sadly, it is part of our predicament that sections of society appear to have embraced this new value system with the mistaken conviction that it encourages loveless sex, mindless violence, and a selfish search for material wealth. Perhaps this teaches us the folly of simply repudiating old standards. We need rather a shift of emphasis and the opportunity to incorporate new values, intelligently and appropriately, into our emerging society. It is clear that these new values have far-reaching implications for the helping professions; and they sound a challenge to the Church, the educational system, the law-makers, and indeed to the whole way we organize our lives.

Sociologists have been pointing out for years that there is a clear mismatch between technological processes and social processes. We seem to lack a culture which is congruent with the needs of our turbulent society, a society characterized by uncertainty and increasing complexity. Trist and Emery[57] suggest that our present organizations and methods are unsuitable for meeting the demands of our environment. They ask for a larger measure of sharing and trust, which will enable a greater pooling of resources. They go on to say: 'Appropriate emergent values . . . may be expected to be communal rather than individualistic regarding access to amenities, co-operative rather than competitive regarding the use of scarce resources; yet personal rather than conforming regarding life styles and goals.' This seems entirely appropriate to the ambitions of a mental health service, which must seek greater co-operation between disciplines and more willingness to share skills and resources, while at the same time maintaining respect for individual differences in aims, methods, and needs.

Dekker[58] has also urged a recognition of our present social crisis and what he describes as 'an overrating of science and technology, a social compulsion towards production, work and consumption with, as the ultimate result, an alienation of people from their own individual potentialities, their fellow-men and society'. In this recognition of our uncertain future and the necessity for intelligent planning, one relevant aim for mental health workers is to call a halt to a society built for passive 'consumers'. People must be encouraged to be active, critical, and creative. Yet experience demonstrates that the mental health system, by itself, has little power. To a large extent mental health institutions have been prisoners of their own culture. Their power structure has been maladaptive. They have failed to produce a cutting-edge for rapid change even in their own field. But there are signs that mental health workers are bursting through traditional boundaries and are becoming increasingly involved with a society whose problems underlie much that is labelled mental illness, deviance, or crime. It may be that, since not many administrators or politicians speak the language of mental health, some of us must learn to speak theirs and, in this way, encourage reform.

Throughout these pages there are implications that knowledge and skill are important, but that they are not the sole prerogative of the professional. Moreover, it is evident that crises occur not only in individuals but also in families, neighbourhoods, and total societies. Staggering from one crisis to the next is no way to run any system. Planning is necessary — planning of an open and innovative kind, which recognizes the impossibility of reaching certainty or completeness, and which tries to mobilize resources in a sharing way. Professional knowledge and leadership are necessary, but planning involves people. It might be said that society's mental health is too important a matter to be left in the hands of professionals. But what the latter can do is give clarity and direction to the strategies involved in planning for comprehensive mental health care. Indeed, suitable models are already available and have been in evidence in the London Borough of Newham,[59] in Craigmillar, Edin - burgh,[60, 61] in Denver, Colorado,[62] and in the Scottish Borders.[63, 64] All such projects (and there are others not cited here) have laid emphasis upon coordination of services inside and outside hospital, continuity of care, and the value of community resources in the prevention of breakdown and hospitalization.

Jones[65] has challenged present-day psychiatrists, formulating the basic question as follows: 'Is psychiatry's function to treat patients individually or in groups, or has it a responsibility to become involved in social problem areas, integrating its skills with other disciplines, e.g. behavioural science, education, religion, architecture, town planning, politics, and so on?' It is clear that if psychiatry accepts such a challenge, it will also have to accept its own ignorance and be prepared to learn from others, not least from clients themselves. Such a movement — more than any formal training scheme — would bring meaning and reality to mental health in the community.

It must be confessed that, in its history of preoccupation with the individual patient, its alliance with 'scientific' medicine, its concern with physical causation and treatment, and its emphasis on doctor as therapist, psychiatry has neglected important areas. One is the patient's own social system. Somehow a person's internal environment, his place in his family, and his role in an organization, need to match one another. When these sub-systems fail to match, it is then that symptoms arise, behaviour becomes disturbed, a crisis looms, and help may be sought. Also it becomes increasingly evident how important the family is as a social system with its own characteristic stresses and resources. As an arena for effective intervention it has been relatively neglected. But in fact it is an obvious meeting-place for professionals concerned with mental health — social worker, health visitor, G.P., and others. How useful it would be if they met with a degree of common understanding, training, and knowledge of family processes! Training schemes already exist for the new 'mental health worker' whose education and role will transcend traditional disciplinary boundaries. Meantime much could be achieved by a joint learning process in the training of doctor, nurse, and social worker. Perhaps room might also be found for clergyman, teacher, and lawyer.

Above all the professional must remember that the patient himself, the person in trouble, who was a productive citizen yesterday and can be again tomorrow, has his own resources, responsibilities, and contributions to make. It is demonstrably foolish to plan *for* people. We must learn to plan *with* them.

REFERENCES

1. GLASSCOTE, R. M. *et al. The Psychiatric Emergency,* The Joint Information Service of A.P.A. and N.A.M.H., Washington. (1966).

2. MORRICE, J. K. W. Emergency psychiatry, *Brit. J. Psychiat.* 114, 485. (1968).

3. MORRICE, J. K. W. Life crisis, social diagnosis, and social therapy, *Brit. J. Psychiat.* 125, 411. (1974).

4. KESSEL, N. Self-poisoning, *Brit. Med. J.* 2, 1265, 1336 (1965).

5. JACOBSON, S. and TRIBE, P. Deliberate self-injury (attempted suicide) in patients admitted to hospital in mid-Sussex, *Brit. J. Psychiat.* 121, 379. (1972).

6. KENNEDY, P. and KREITMAN, N. An epidemiological survey of parasuicides (attempted suicide), *Brit. J. Psychiat.* 123, 23. (1973).

7. WHITE, H. C. Self-poisoning in adolescents, *Brit. J. Psychiat.* 124, 24. (1974).

8. SHNEIDMAN, E. S. and FARBEROW, N. L. *Clues to Suicide,* McGraw-Hill, New York. (1957).

9. FARBEROW, N. L. and SHNEIDMAN, E. S. *A Cry for Help,* McGraw-Hill, New York. (1961).

10. CAPLAN, G. *Principles of Preventive Psychiatry,* Tavistock Publ., London. (1964).

11. CAPLAN, G. *An Approach to Community Mental Health,* Tavistock Publ., London. (1961).

12. ARIE, T. Dementia in the elderly, *Brit. Med. J.* 4, 540, 602. (1973).

13. KAY, D., BEAMISH, P., and ROTH, M. Old age mental disorders in Newcastle upon Tyne, *Brit. J. Psychiat.* 110, 146. (1964).

14. WILLIAMSON, J., STOKOE, I., GRAY, S., *et al.* Old people at home: their unreported needs, *Lancet,* 1, 1117. (1964).

15. *Services for the Elderly with Mental Disorder,* Report of a sub-committee of the Standing Medical Advisory Committee, Scottish Home & Health Dept. H.M.S.O. (1970).

16. *Mental Health Services of Local Health Authorities,* Report by the Standing Advisory Committee on Local Authority Services. H.M.S.O. (1961).

17. *A Hospital Plan for England and Wales,* H.M.S.O. (1962).

18. PARKES C.M. *Bereavement: Studies of Grief in Adult Life,* Tavistock Publ., London. (1972).

19. FREUD, S. Mourning and melancholia, in *Collected Papers,* Vol. IV, Hogarth Press, London. (1950).

20. COBB, S. and LINDEMANN, E. Symposium on management of Coconut Grove burns at Massachusetts General Hospital: neuro-psychiatric observations, *Ann. Surg.* 117, 814. (1943).

21. LINDEMANN, E. Symptomatology and management of acute grief, *Am. J. Psychiat.* 101, 141. (1944).

22. BOWLBY, J. Processes of mourning, *Int. J. Psychoanal.* 42, 317. (1961).

23. PARKES, C. M. The first year of bereavement, *Psychiat.* 33, 444. (1971).

24. GORER, G. *Death, Grief and Mourning in Contemporary Britain,* Cresset, London. (1965).

25. HINTON, J. *Dying,* Penguin Books, Harmondsworth. (1967).

26. COWIE, J. The school counsellor and the child guidance clinic, in *Guidance and Counselling in British Schools,* ed. Lytton, H. and Craft, M., Edward Arnold Ltd., London. (1969).

27. GIBBENS, T. C. N., PALMER, C., and PRINCE, J. Mental health aspects of shoplifting, *Brit. Med. J.* 3, 612. (1971).

28. HOLT, J. *The Underachieving School,* Penguin Books, Harmondsworth. (1971).

29. MORRIS, B. An educational perspective on mental health, in *Towards Community Mental Health,* ed. Sutherland, J. D., Tavistock Publ., London. (1971).

30. BALINT, M., and BALINT, E. *Psychotherapeutic Techniques in Medicine,* Tavistock Publ., London. (1961).

31. SUTHERLAND, J. D. Psychoanalysis in the post-industrial society, *Inter. J. Psychoanal.* **50**, 673. (1969).

32. THOMPSON, S. and KAHN, J. H. *The Group Process as a Helping Technique,* Pergamon Press, Oxford. (1970).

33. MORRICE, J. K. W. A day hospital's function in a mental health service, *Brit. J. Psychiat.* **122**, 307. (1973).

34. Morbidity Statistics from General Practice: Second National Study 1970 - 1971, *Studies on Medical and Population Subjects No. 26.* H.M.S.O. (1974).

35. FRY, J. *Common Diseases: their nature, incidence and care,* Medical and Technical Publ. Lancaster. (1974).

36. STEVENS, J. Hypnotics – A G.P.'s view, *Prescribers' J.* **13**, 104. (1973).

37. MAY, A. R. and GREGORY, E. Participation of general practitioners in community psychiatry, *Brit. Med. J.* **2**, 168. (1968).

38. KAHN, J. H. Occupied territories, *Marriage Guid. Bull.* **15**, 88. (1974).

39. *Young Adult Offenders,* Report by the Home Office Advisory Council on the Penal System. H.M.S.O. (1974).

40. SILBERMAN, C. E. *Crisis in the Classroom,* Random House, New York. (1970).

41. EISELEY, L. *The Night Country,* Garnstone Press, London. (1974).

42. CRAFT, M. Guidance, counselling and social needs, in *Guidance and Counselling in British Schools,* ed. Lytton, H. and Craft, M., Edward Arnold Ltd., London. (1969).

43. *Keeping Pace with Tomorrow,* Report of the special commission on priorities of mission in Scotland in the 1970's. Church of Scotland.

44. MILLS, A. *Pre-Crisis Care,* Committee on Moral Welfare, Church of Scotland. (1973).

45. BURNETT, P. S. The social sciences and the work of the churches, *The Expository Times,* **81**, 132. (1970).

46. FLETCHER, J. *Situation Ethics,* Westminster Press, Philadelphia. (1966).

47. MORRICE, J.K.W. Don't step on the underdog: a personal view of the psychiatric nurse, *Nursing Times,* **66**, 766. (1970).

48. STOBIE, E. G., and HOPKINS, D. Crisis intervention: a psychiatric community nurse in a rural area, *Nursing Times,* **68**, 165, 169. (1972).

49. HENDERSON, J. G., LEVEN, B., and CHEYNE, E. The role of the psychiatric nurse in domiciliary treatment service, *Nursing Times,* **69**, 1334 *et seq.* (1973).

50. CUMMINGS, E., *et al.* The policeman as philosopher, guide and friend, *Social Problems,* **12**, 276. (1965).

51. PUNCH, M., and NAYLOR, T. The police: a social service, *New Society,* 17 May. (1973).

52. CAIN, M. *Society and the Policeman's Role,* Routledge & Kegan Paul, London. (1973).

53. MacFADYEN, J. Working paper: the police as a social service, Scottish Police College. (1974).

54. LORD GIFFORD, quoted in Free legal advice in the High Street, *The Observer,* 19 May. (1974).

55. EISENBERG, L. The future of psychiatry, *Lancet,* **2**, 1371. (1973).

56. SCHON, D. *Beyond the Stable State,* Temple Smith, London. (1971).

57. EMERY, F. E., and TRIST, E. L. *Towards a Social Ecology,* Plenum Press, London. (1972).

58. DEKKER, E. Change as a value, a tool and an objective for mental health; paper delivered at W.F.M.H., Amsterdam. (1972).

59. KAHN, J. H. A pioneer scheme in community mental health, *Nursing Mirror,* 12 Feb. (1971).

60. EBIE, J. C. *et al.* An integrated approach to a community's health and social problems, *Health Bull.* **28**, 35. (1970).

61. SAVEGE, J. Community psychiatry in Edinburgh, *Focus,* July. (1972).

62. KRAFT, A. M. The Fort Logan mental health center, *Milbank Memorial Fund Quarterly,* **44**, 19. (1966).

63. JONES, M. *Beyond the Therapeutic Community,* Yale Univ. Press, New Haven and London. (1968).

64. MORRICE, J. K. W. Dingleton Hospital's therapeutic community, *Hosp. and Community Psychiat.* (A.P.A.), May. (1966).

65. JONES, M. Psychiatry, systems theory, education, and change. *Brit. J. Psychiat.* **124**, 75. (1974).

INDEX

117